Surviving Wildfire

Get Prepared
Stay Alive
Rebuild Your Life

LINDA MASTERSON

PIXYJACK PRESS INC

SURVIVING WILDFIRE: GET PREPARED, STAY ALIVE, REBUILD YOUR LIFE
(A HANDBOOK FOR HOMEOWNERS)

Published by PixyJack Press, Inc
PO Box 149, Masonville, CO 80541 USA

Paperback ISBN 978-1-936555-15-4
Kindle ISBN 978-1-936555-16-1
ePub ISBN 978-1-936555-17-8

Library of Congress Cataloging-in-Publication-Data
Masterson, Linda (Linda J.)
  Surviving wildfire : get prepared, stay alive, rebuild your life : a handbook for homeowners / by Linda Masterson.
       pages cm
  Includes index.
  Summary:"Covers what to do before, during, and after wildfire disasters. Advice for homeowners includes advance preparations for land, home and family; evacuation essentials and survival strategies when wildfire threatens; understanding insurance; and rebuilding and recovery"-- Provided by publisher.
  ISBN 978-1-936555-15-4
  1. Dwellings--Fires and fire prevention--United States. 2. Wildfires--United States.
I. Title.
  TH9445.D9M37 2013
  613.6'9--dc23
                         2012042282

To view these photos in color, please visit www.SurvivingWildfire.com

For Cory, always
and for the survivor in us all

CONTENTS

Foreword

There's nothing quite like knowing that you are probably about to die, no matter what you do in the minute or two you have left. It is a realization that brings into sharp focus every survival instinct you never knew you had. *Move! Get out! Now!* you scream inside your head, even though you find yourself staring into a void filled with flame and smoke and you know your only chance of living through the night is to drive blindly into it and out the other side. Except you don't really know if there is another side, or if it's possible to reach it without driving off the narrow winding road, or running into a downed tree, or succumbing to the hot poisonous gases that have all around you replaced the cool oxygen-rich air your lungs crave. All you know is you're out of options, so even though you can't see one square inch of road, you push on, mixing caution and haste in what you pray is a workable combination...

It's the stuff of nightmares. But this was a nightmare my wife, LaVonne, and I somehow lived through shortly after midnight on April 2, 2011, just about the time the home author Linda Masterson shared with her husband, Cory Phillips, was being reduced to a pile of ashes. Dozens of lives were irrevocably changed that night, but while the others struggle to put it all behind them, Linda somehow dug down deep and found the courage to face her demons eye to eye in the single hope that she might be able to help others avoid what she and Cory had to endure. And, if your home is destroyed, to confront the seemingly endless trauma that comes in a wildfire's wake as if it were a bump in the road rather than a final destination. "You *will* get through this," Linda promises; life goes on, albeit differently.

It is rare for someone as intimately involved as Linda to deal methodically and systematically with the subject of personal disaster, and it gives *Surviving Wildfire* that distinct flavor of authenticity a book like this ought to have; a passion that shines behind the facts and figures and down-to-earth advice on how to prepare yourself for the unthinkable. And how to pick up the pieces of your life and begin the process of recovery should it actually happen.

This book's small size belies the mountain of crucial information it offers those of us living where wildfire can take our homes, our treasured possessions, and even our lives. No matter what your level of expertise in dealing with wildfire and its aftermath, your knowledge of the subject will be greatly enriched by reading this book. Some of it is surprising, some of it ingenious. All of it is useful. The biggest eye-opener for me? Never try to drive through a flame front; it's too hot and you probably won't make it. Let it pass, then proceed with caution. If providence had not already intervened the night of April 2, it is advice that would have saved our lives.

— Rex Ewing

Introduction

What would you do if you had fifteen minutes to leave your home, and you knew it might not be standing when you came back? What would you take? Where would you go? How would you make sure everyone got out safely?

If you lost your home, what would you wish you'd done differently? Could you have done anything to save it? Would you have enough insurance? What's covered, and what isn't? Where would you live? And where do you start when you need to rebuild your life from scratch?

My husband Cory and I learned the answers to all those questions and many more the hard way. Our home in the foothills west of Fort Collins, Colorado burned to the ground one night in April 2011, along with the homes of twelve of our neighbors.

We were better prepared than most. But we were nowhere near as well prepared as we should have been. Or could have been.

Losing your home and everything you own is such a profoundly life-altering experience that even now it's hard for me to find words to describe it. There's just this huge, gaping hole where your life used to be. When people ask if you need anything, it's hard to know what to say. Because you need everything. During those first few terrible weeks our friends and families were the glue that held us together. We would have crumbled without their constant help and support.

When our mental fog began to clear, we decided that since Mother Nature had wiped our slate clean, we'd use it as an opportunity to reinvent ourselves from the ground up. Because looking backwards gets you nowhere.

I agreed to write this handbook because I don't want anyone else to learn their lessons the way we had to. I've spent much of my professional life researching, writing and explaining all sorts of things. So I gathered up and sifted through a bewildering array of materials from all manner of experts so you don't have to. And assembled resources that will help you dig deeper.

With this book you'll learn how to make your home and property as fire-resistant as possible without having to live in a bunker on top of a rock pile. You'll be able to analyze your insurance needs and document your life now, so you'll know you have the right coverage and the right information before you need it. You'll discover practical ways to live more safely and smartly with the threat of wildfire, and what to do when every second counts.

And whether you're one of the unlucky ones whose home has been damaged or destroyed or you just want to know what to expect and how your insurance really works, you'll find information and insights on every aspect of recovery, from who to call first to how to wade through your contents inventory.

I hope you'll find this book useful, practical and eye-opening. More than anything, I hope our story of loss and recovery will motivate you to do what you can now to prepare your home and your life "just in case."

CHAPTER 1

Wildfire: A Growing Problem

Over the past decade the number of homes and other structures lost to wildfires each year has more than tripled. From 1985 through 2000, an average of 400 homes were destroyed in wildfires each year. Between 2001 and 2011 the annual average jumped to 1,354 homes. And as the number of megafires grows, global wildfire experts expect the number of homes destroyed each year to continue to climb.

Megafires aren't just big—typically 100,000 acres or more—they're very destructive and often deadly. They usually develop when conditions are just right for fires to grow quickly beyond any hope of control, in areas where there are plenty of fuels to burn and the weather is hot, dry and windy. In the U.S. only about one to two percent of all wildfires grow into behemoths that are large and destructive enough to qualify, but these megafires gobble up more than 95% of all the acres burned and 85% of the money spent fighting wildfires. And they often destroy homes not by the dozens, but by the hundreds.

In 2011 there were more than 74,000 wildfires in the U.S. They burned in every state in except Delaware. Forest, grass and brush fires destroyed 3,459 homes and 1,800 other structures and damaged countless more. Wildfires burned over 8.7 million acres and caused $1.9 billion in economic losses.

In terms of the sheer number of fires, 2011 was slightly below the ten-year average. But in terms of destruction, it was the third worst year since they started keeping records back in the 1960s. Even more sobering is the fact that six of the top ten worst years for wildfire have all occurred since the turn of the 21st century.

"We've been in a long drought cycle for the last 20 years, and conditions now are great for these type of fires," said Steve Pyne, author of

Tending Fire: Coping with America's Wildland Fires and a life science professor at Arizona State University.

The wildfire season got off to an early start in 2012, when a fast-moving brush fire near Reno, Nevada, destroyed 20 homes and forced the evacuation of 10,000 people in January. In late March a controlled burn meant to reduce fire danger and presumed to be out reignited in the hills southwest of Denver and quickly grew into the deadly Lower North Fork fire that killed three people and destroyed 23 homes.

By April, after one of the driest winters in the East on record, hundreds of wildfires were burning in New Jersey, New York, Connecticut, Maryland, Delaware, Pennsylvania, Virginia, West Virginia and Florida. In May the Whitewater-Baldy blaze scorched more than 300 square miles in New Mexico, on its way to becoming the largest wildfire in the state's history. The Duck Lake fire on Michigan's Upper Peninsula raged over 20,000 acres, destroying 34 homes, a motel, a store and countless outbuildings.

Then for three long weeks in June while I was working on this book, the High Park Fire near my new home outside of Fort Collins, Colorado burned more than 136 square miles. I watched with a terrible sense of déjà vu as it claimed the homes of 259 of my friends and former neighbors and took one woman's life. Eight volunteer firefighters defended the homes of their neighbors while their own homes burned to the ground.

The High Park Fire was the most destructive wildfire in Colorado history for just two weeks until the world watched in disbelief as the Waldo Canyon fire near Colorado Springs threatened the U.S. Air Force Academy, swept into suburban neighborhoods and consumed a mind-numbing 347 homes in just two days, leaving two more victims dead in the ashes.

By late summer, the 2012 fire season was on track to be the deadliest and most destructive in history, with over 7 million acres burned, 1,800 structures destroyed and at least 24 people killed—with a third of the fire "season" left to go. On one Saturday in August there were 33 wildfires burning over a million acres in ten states. Ten large new wildfires were reported in just one day; three in Montana, two in Oklahoma and one each in Arizona, Florida, Idaho, Kansas and South Dakota.

Research shows that many of the most destructive wildfires of late have been started by people who had no idea that what they were doing would unleash an inferno. Such as unattended campfires fanned back to life by the wind; slash pile burns that got away; ATVs, lawnmowers and power tools that threw sparks into dry grass; cars with hot tail pipes driving through grass; bullets striking a rock and creating a spark; road equipment hitting a boulder with the same results; and cigarettes thrown out the car window. Motor vehicle accidents or house fires ignite wildfires as do downed power lines. Some wildfires started out as controlled (prescribed) burns set by authorities to reduce fire danger that get out of control and can't be stopped. A few wildfires are started intentionally by arsonists. And a few are still ignited the old fashioned way, by Mother Nature's arsenal of lighting bolts and lava flows.

Wildland firefighters and other emergency personnel are well-trained. They know the risks. They're armed with the latest equipment and safety devices. They have access to up-to-the-minute weather, infrared heat sensors and sophisticated eyes-in-the-sky. And yet every year on average 18 of these brave and resourceful men and women die.

Little wonder that most years civilians die too. People trapped in their homes and cars. People cut off from their only escape route. People who ignored evacuation orders and stayed to defend their homes, armed with a garden hose and a shovel. People who underestimated how big the fire was, how fast it could move and where it was going. People who waited too long by their phones for evacuation orders that came too late, or not at all. People who took too much time trying to save their pets or livestock or belongings. People who didn't think the fire could ever reach them.

Why the Threat of Wildfire is Growing

The population of the U.S. has nearly tripled over the past century. Over the past few decades, millions of people have moved out of the cities and suburbs and into wilder places with more space, better views and what people hope will be a better quality of life.

Meanwhile a warming climate, frequent intense droughts, record heat, widespread insect infestations that turn live trees into standing-dead firewood and a century of vigorous fire suppression have all contributed to creating overgrown, densely packed second-growth forests and brushlands that have long been deprived of Mother's Nature normal clean-up and clear-out process of renewal: periodic wildfires.

Even if the intertwined labyrinth of federal, state and local agencies and entities in charge of America's fire suppression and fire management programs all agreed today that it would be best in the long run to let nature take its fiery course, it wouldn't be possible to take the leap from theory to reality. That's because today communities large and small are twined through all those wild places, creating an incredibly complex landscape of homes and subdivisions strung out along the fringes of natural areas or tucked into the mosaic of private property interspersed between public lands.

People may be happy to leave the hustle and bustle of the city, but they often pack up their city and suburban attitudes and expectations and bring them along. But life on the wilder side comes with its own rulebook; one that's filled with all sorts of things most people have never even thought about.

No one wants to think about wildfire when they're shopping for property or building or buying their dream home. And even if they do, they often assume that the fire department will be there, as always, to protect them from disaster. Firefighters do get most wildfires under control fairly quickly. But under the right conditions, winds can whip a fire into an inferno that can neither be controlled nor contained.

When an extreme wildfire is raging, dozens or hundreds or even thousands of homes can be in its path. There will never be enough equipment or personnel to defend every home in danger. Sometimes conditions make it impossible for responders to even reach homes that are at risk.

Wildland firefighters wish it were possible to save every home in a fire's path. But it's not. So it's the homes that are most defendable that are defended when possible. And it's the homes that are the most fire-resistant that have the best chance of surviving on their own.

Factors Affecting Fire Behavior

Every wildfire is different. But every wildfire is affected by the same three things: fuel, weather and terrain. You can't do anything about the weather except understand how weather impacts a fire and keep on top of the forecast. But you can reduce available fuel near your home, and take your terrain into account when you're buying, building or improving.

1) Fuel

Fuel is literally anything that burns. Whether it's natural fuels like grasses, pine needles, bushes or trees or human-provided fuels like fences, sheds, deck railings, furniture and your house, if it can catch on fire, it's fuel.

Fuel load is how much fuel is available for the fire to consume; it's usually measured in tons per unit, typically per acre. The greater the fuel load, the higher the potential for an intense fire. Fires burning in low fuel load areas tend to spread much more slowly than fires burning in high fuel load areas. Look out the window; if your property is carpeted with dense stands of pines and firs and combustible underbrush, you've got a high fuel load.

Fine fuels are dead grasses, leaves, pine needles and other tinder; they catch fire quickly and easily and spread fire faster than coarse fuels like dead twigs and branches. That's why keeping your grass cut, your bushes pruned and your gutters and eaves clear of debris is so important. The drier the fuels, the faster they'll burn, and the harder it can be to get the fire under control.

Surface fuels are on the ground; dry grasses, shrubs, pine needles, dead branches and twigs. Duff is a layer of several years worth of decomposing woody materials between the pine needles and the ground. A surface fire can burn out the duff and other vegetation without destroying taller trees. Surface fires are usually less intense, but they can travel quickly and put homes at risk if there's a continuous path of fuels that act like a wick and carry fire up to the house.

Ladder fuels are just what they sound like. They're taller brush, low hanging branches and anything else that can carry fire from the ground up into the tops or crowns of trees and tall shrubs. Ladder fuels include things like that hammock you have hanging from your favorite tree.

Crown fuels are the flammable tops of trees and tall shrubs, also known as the canopy. A fire that gets into a canopy that stretches for miles is the most dangerous type of wildfire, because it can hopscotch quickly from tree to tree and spread very rapidly. With so much fuel, crown fires burn extremely hot, and create radiant heat so intense that things can burst into flames while the fire is still many yards away.

2) Terrain

A wildfire can run uphill four to five times faster than downhill. That's because wind travels uphill, taking the fire along with it. That super-heated air acts like a gigantic hair dryer on the fuels in front of it as it moves, making it easier for them to catch on fire. A fire burning uphill also has longer flames that shoot further up into the air. Anything on the upslope that can burn just feeds the fire's intensity and speeds up the spread. Draws and canyons act like funnels for the fire, channeling flames, intensifying heat and sending a roaring column of fire racing to the top.

3) Weather

Understanding how the weather impacts wildfire can help you do a better job of evaluating the day-to-day risk and knowing what to do if a wildfire threatens. For instance, if there are multiple lightning strikes in a torrential downpour, there's much less chance of a fire igniting and surviving than if there's a high-based gusty thunderstorm with lots of lightning and ground strikes but very little rain.

Drought creates extremely favorable conditions for a wildfire; the drier the fuels, the easier they are to ignite, and the faster they burn. Drought affects the moisture content of everything from flowers, plants and trees to your house.

Heat also plays a big part; the hotter the fuels are to start with, the faster they will reach the internal temperature where all their moisture is gone and they burst into flames. This is one reason wildfires always seem to be at their most destructive in the heat of the afternoon. It's the same reason fires "lie down" at night. As temperatures cool, winds shift and humidity rises, which usually slows the progress of the fire.

Wind is probably the biggest single factor in how fast and how far a wildfire will spread. Wind pushes flames and brings oxygen, the lifeblood of every fire. Strong winds can carry firebrands and embers for a mile or more. In an active firestorm, thousands of flaming embers can come raining down out of the sky to start hundreds of new spot fires.

Fires also create their own weather. Massive wildfires can actually generate winds, which are often called fire whirls (tornadoes that are spawned by the vortex created by the heat of the fire). Fire whirls can hurl not just embers but flaming logs and debris for long distances. Wind gusts can carry flames up into the crowns of trees. Wind direction can also be highly unpredictable and changeable, especially in mountainous terrain or when fronts are moving through or the weather is transitioning from one season to another.

....

Sign-Up for Weather Alerts

Many television stations offer custom forecasts on their websites that are based on your GPS coordinates or address. Some will even call you if there is a severe weather alert for your area. Knowing when winds will come up or whether or not there is any precipitation in the forecast can be a big help when you are tracking a fire. Or just planning a picnic.

....

How Homes Catch Fire

According to fire research scientist Jack Cohen, embers and firebrands are the leading causes of homes catching fire in a wildfire. Firebrands are burning materials that literally detach from a fire and are carried on the wind or the strong convection drafts that the fire creates. Airborne firebrands can travel more than a mile before dropping from the sky to kindle fires wherever they land. When firebrands land on flammable roofs or decks, they can ignite leaves and needles on the roof, in the gutters, under decks, and on porches. Then it's only a matter of time before flames find their way inside. Clearing debris and sealing openings and vents can make your home better able to take the heat.

Surface and ground fires can also start homes on fire. Light fuels like tall dried grasses can turn into a fuse and lead the fire straight to your home. Winds can make a surface fire move at a heart-stopping pace.

If there are tall grasses and shrubs close to trees, they can give the fire a ladder to climb up into the lower branches, and from there up to the crown. If the crowns of trees are close together, fire will hopscotch very quickly from tree to tree, creating a gigantic flame front that generates so much radiant heat a house can seemingly burst into flames from as far as 200 feet away. It's radiant heat that's responsible for most of those instances where people swear something "burst into flames." Radiant heat can also break windows or melt things like vinyl siding, doors or shutters, allowing heat and/or firebrands into your home.

Take a good look at the 200 feet surrounding your home, and try to imagine everything on fire. How many heavy fuel sources like stands of tall dense trees or shrubs, firewood piles, parked vehicles or a nearby home or outbuilding are there? Anything within 200 feet that could burn for a long time can throw off enough radiant heat to catch your home on fire. By following the Firewise guidelines, reducing the fuel around your home and putting in fire breaks like irrigated lawns and gardens, pathways, and gravel or rock mulch, you can deprive a wildfire of the fuel it needs.

You can't stop a wildfire. And you can't do anything about the weather or your topography. But your building materials, maintenance and defensible landscape (chapters 3 and 4) play a major role in determining just how much exposure your home can take before the flames even reach it.

Faster than a Speeding Wildfire

Wildfires can move through a forest at speeds approaching seven miles per hour; fire can move through grasslands more than twice as fast. A fire in the chaparral in August can throw out flames nearly 50 feet long. Surface winds and slope play a big part in how fast a fire will spread, but once the fire is burning intensely, it makes its own weather. An actively burning wildfire can create wind speeds up to ten times higher than winds immediately outside the fire area. In the time it takes you to run from your bedroom to the garage a fast-moving wildfire can easily travel from two miles away to your doorstep. There are few sights more terrifying than a wildfire racing towards you.

What you do long before a wildfire threatens can give your home and your community a much better chance of surviving. What you do when fire is approaching can literally make the difference between life and death.

CHAPTER 2

Assessing Your Risk

Do You Live in the Wildfire Zone?

If you live within two miles of a natural area, you live in what fire experts call the WUI, the Wildland Urban Interface Zone. If you live within a mile, you live in the Ember Zone; burning embers can travel at least that far on the wind. Embers from the fire that destroyed our home were hurled by hurricane-force winds gusting to 90 mph. They traveled well over a mile as the ember flies, and when they finally rained down they started another wildfire that threatened more homes.

The interagency working definition of the WUI (pronounced WOO-EE) is any area with both human presence and wildland vegetation. It includes forests, native grasslands, shrubs, wetlands, and lands in transition, like clearcuts. It doesn't include anything that's been altered by humans, including urban grasslands like golf courses, orchards, farms and pastures. Is your home tucked into a brush-covered hillside? Are you nestled in the foothills? Can you go hiking out your back door? Do you gaze out over the grasslands? You live in the WUI.

The National Association of State Foresters (NASF) continually surveys all states to try and identify communities at risk and develop Community Wildfire Protection Plans. While not its main purpose, this continuous report helps provide a national snapshot of wildfire risk. And it's not a pretty picture: the 2011 report shows 66,700 communities at risk across the country. Across the U.S. 9.4% of all land is classified as WUI and all states have at least some WUI.

For some states, three-quarters of their land is in the WUI. In 19 of the contiguous 48 states, more than half of all homes are in the WUI. In the ever more populous Rocky Mountains and the Southwest, virtually every urban area is surrounded by a big ring of WUI, with mile after mile of medium-and low-density housing near or in low-elevation forested areas. In fire-prone California, over 5.1 million homes are built in the WUI.

If you already live in the WUI, this book will give you the information and motivation you need to take a fresh look at your home and property, and to start making the changes that could help save your home and your life if a wildfire threatens.

If you're contemplating a move, you'll be able to evaluate your options for more than scenic views and privacy. If you're building, you'll be armed with the info you need to help you carefully select and improve the most defensible site and choose materials and features that will give you and your new home a better chance of surviving a fire.

Examining Your Danger Zone

There is no national map with property-level detail that shows wildfire risk; I know, because I talked to about 20 various national and regional agencies and associations involved in some aspect of fire management trying to find one. But there are regional risk maps for the South and West. The Southern Group of State Foresters has an extensive and detailed website *(www. southernforests.org)* with loads of information, and a tool that will allow you to map your address for wildfire risk. Texas recently unveiled an interactive online tool that lets you get right down to your address and check out your

A California home survives in the midst of acres and acres of blackened landscape.

risk. Many states where wildfires are a fact of life have maps or ratings on either a state or county basis.

Some areas in the WUI are at high wildfire risk; some are not. Risk can vary within a county or even a subdivision. Understanding your personal risk will help you make better choices.

Every state has a state forest, and most have wildfire information and people who deal with fire. Talk to the public information officer and find out what kind of assistance they can provide in assessing your risk. In many cases a forester or fire expert will come out and visit your home or property for free. They can give you an on-the-ground assessment of your situation, and suggest steps you can take to improve your defensibility.

If you own more than an acre or two, the hazard level can vary greatly from the lower-risk area down in a valley on the north side by a year-round creek to the high hazard area up on top of a steep juniper-covered south-facing slope. Variations within a community can be even greater. Knowing where you stand can help you choose the smartest place to build.

What's Your Wildfire Risk?

What's wrong with this picture?

The national Firewise guidelines will help you do a preliminary evalua-tion of your hazard level. You can often find more localized information on community and association risk assessments, specific types of vegeta-tion, and other local factors on your state forest's or county's website. You can also contact your local fire department or state forestry office for help assessing your specific location.

Low hazard areas have primarily short grasses, low growing non-resinous shrubs and plants that don't have woody stems, like groundcover and perennials. Trees are mainly deciduous species like aspens, poplar, maple, oak and beech rather than evergreens and pines. Greenbelts are not continuous; instead they're broken up by urban or clustered development. There are lots of firebreaks like roads, utility easements, lakes and ponds or large tracts of irrigated land. Climate: Generally humid, with a short dry season. Sometimes it's hot, dry and windy, but not every year, and not for long stretches of time.

Medium hazard areas are filled with wildlands throughout the community. There are tall, heavy grasses and many small, flammable shrubs with woody stems, low-growing evergreens like pines, junipers and yews and plants that are woody, waxy or resinous. There are more shrubs than deciduous trees. Climate: Dry, windy conditions are common at least once a year. There's a predictable dry season or the area is in a prolonged drought.

High hazard areas consist of dense forest (including dead or dying trees) with a great amount of dense, highly flammable vegetation. The tops of trees form a practically unbroken canopy, and there are lots of medium to tall shrubs and coniferous bushes like junipers and yews. Climate: It's often dry and windy. The dry season lasts more than three months, or the area is in a prolonged drought.

....

About Firewise®

The National Fire Protection Association's (NFPA) Firewise Communities program focuses on encouraging local solutions designed to help everyone from homeowners to community leaders prepare for and do a better job of protecting people and property from wildfire risk. They teach people how to adapt to living with wildfire risk and encourages neighbors to work together and take action now to prevent losses. Extensive resources for homeowners, communities and associations, developers and firefighters can be found on their user-friendly website at *www.firewise.org,* along with many reference materials you can download, presentations and interactive modules. The program is cosponsored by the USDA Forest Service, the U.S. Department of the Interior, and the National Association of State Foresters.

....

CHAPTER 3

Improving Your Odds

The potential for catastrophic, uncontrollable wildfires grows every year. Fire risk in the WUI and what we can do as a nation to reduce it has of late become a subject of intense scrutiny and study. The amount of information out there is overwhelming. But a couple of simple facts stand out in stark relief. Upwards of 65% of all homes now built in the WUI nationwide are in high-fire hazard areas.

A recent study by Headwaters Economics shows that in 11 fire-prone Western states, only about 14% of the land in the WUI has actually been developed, leaving 86% available for future development. And so the potential for catastrophic fires that gobble up homes is going to continue to grow.

In high fire-hazard areas, it's not a question of "if" wildfires will occur, but a question of "when." And of what people can do to live more safely in a fire-prone environment.

Before You Buy Property

We moved to Colorado from a suburb of Chicago with neighbors so close we could have passed coffeecake back and forth. We'd been escaping to the wilds for years. So when we went shopping for property, we insisted on plenty of trees for privacy and great views. That's how we ended up on top of a ridge with panoramic views of overgrown forest in all directions— which we now realize was one of the most wildfire-susceptible places we could have built.

So if you're shopping for property, call the State Forest Service and ask about both fire history and risk for the future. Talk to the county building department and find out if they do wildfire safety inspections. Where's the nearest fire station? Water supply? A county plat map will show you the road systems and other features. Is there more than one way in and out of the area? You can also check out the view from Google Earth.

If you're considering property that's part of a homeowners association (HOA), read their covenants before you make an offer. Some HOAs have very strict landscaping regulations and may not permit you to cut down trees even to create defensible space. Some covenants may mandate building materials (i.e. wood siding, shake roofs) that put your house at higher wildfire risk.

Talk to your insurance agent and find out what type of coverage is available, and get a ballpark estimate of what good coverage will cost. For more on how to buy insurance, see chapter 5. And don't let your heart rule your head. Before you make an offer, identify at least one potential building site you love that offers maximum protection from wildfire.

Before You Build

It's more cost effective and much easier to site, design and build your home with fire protection in mind than it is to retrofit. So if you're at the dreaming and doodling stage, add "Fire Safety" to your list of must-haves. This is also a good time to ask your insurance agent for a list of building features that can help reduce your premiums; things like a non-combustible or fire-resistant roof and exterior building materials can save you money year after year as well as protect your home. A few things to consider when siting your home:

Avoid Slopes. Build on the most level part of your land. Unlike humans, fire loves to run uphill, and spreads much more rapidly on even minor slopes. The steeper the slope, the faster it runs.

Avoid Edges. A one-story house needs to be at least 30 feet back from any drop off or cliff (unless it's a drop off into a large body of water at the bottom of a rocky cliff). If your home is more than one-story, double your setback. Hate the idea of giving up your fabulous view? Consider a stone patio; you'll be improving your defensibility and giving yourself a great place to soak up the scenery that you won't have to mow, weed or water.

Consider Your Exposure. South and southwest exposures are generally hotter and drier, and prone to having more fires. Slopes that face south are at their hottest and driest in the afternoon, the time that most wildfires make their most aggressive runs.

Know Your Prevailing Winds. A wind-driven fire can travel miles in minutes. If the prevailing winds during your normal active fire season are from the west, you'll want as big a firebreak as possible on the west side of your home.

Create a site plan. Plot out where your house will go, and then add in everything that will be attached to it, such as decks and garages. Anything directly attached to your house should be treated as part of it when you're planning defensible space (see the next chapter). Anything flammable (such as a barn or outbuilding) situated more than 100 feet away from the house will need its own defensible space. Use colored rope to lay out your dream home; then pick another color to outline at least 100 feet of defensible space all around your home site. Careful planning now can help keep you from having to cut down your favorite tree before you can move in.

Trees. If you have trees you want to leave standing close to your home, incorporate them into the footprint, and extend your defensible space out from there. Just be sure there are no branches overhanging your roof; they can offer fire a fast path to your home.

Propane tanks and woodpiles need to be at least 30 feet away from the house. Woodpiles should be downwind and uphill if the land is not level, so that if the woodpile catches on fire, the firebrands travel away from your house. Thinking about this while you're building will help you avoid having to install your propane tank directly in your favorite view. If you own your propane tank, you can always bury it in the ground.

Driveway. Your driveway should be wide enough to allow for the passage of fire trucks and other emergency vehicles. A canopy of trees is romantic and appealing, but trees hanging down over your driveway are a fire hazard and can impede the progress of emergency vehicles; trim tree branches 15 feet up from the ground.

Turnarounds. A circular driveway or parking pad large enough for big vehicles to easily turn around will make your home much more defendable. Firefighters are trained not to enter places where they could be trapped, so having a clear escape route is imperative. In many situations, firefighters cannot even attempt to defend your home if there is no safe way to turn around and exit.

Access roads in the WUI are often privately maintained; our association's one-lane winding road had 700-foot drop-offs in some places, and only a few turnouts to allow for two-way traffic. During our fire we were almost trapped trying to get out by a well-meaning neighbor trying to bring in a horse trailer to help evacuate a friend's horses. That's why guidelines recommend at least a 10-foot clearance on either side of the road, and frequent pullouts and turnouts if the road can't be wide enough for two-way traffic.

Firewise Building

You know how you can never figure out how moths and flies and mice get into your house? Fire slithers in the same way. Fire will exploit any crack, crevice or opening, no matter how small. Its mission in life is to feed itself and grow. You can take a virtual tour of a Firewise home at *www.firewise. org (search under Information and Resources)*. See chapter 1 for how homes ignite and burn in a wildfire.

Use these following tips as a guide when designing a new home. If you're building your own home, take your plans to a fire expert or a local architect for review and input. It might cost a few extra bucks now, but designing with fire in mind will greatly improve the odds your home will be one of the "lucky" ones.

Building Codes. If you are working with an architect or designer, they should be familiar with local building codes, which may dictate everything from acceptable materials to soffit design. If you are serving as your own designer, you'll want to contact the building department and get a copy. Many areas in the WUI now have strict building codes designed to make sure structures are as defensible as possible. California building codes passed in 2008 dictate the usage of fire-smart building materials. Local building codes rule; some counties and municipalities have extensive lists of materials that meet local codes on their websites.

Building Materials. Use fire-resistant and non-combustible materials wherever you can. Fire-resistant means that it takes longer for the material to catch on fire, and it burns with less intensity. Non-combustible refers to materials like stone, brick and stucco that don't ignite. Vinyl siding doesn't burn, but it does melt and when it does, it exposes all the framing to flames. And remember, no one has ever failed to pass a building inspection for using materials that exceed code requirements. You can't completely fire-proof your home, but you can make it much more fire resistant.

Log Homes. Many people dream, as we once did, of building a log home in the woods. You don't have to abandon your dreams. Full logs are remarkably fire resistant, just one class below concrete and stone. A properly built log home is much more fire resistant than the typical frame house, which is the most combustible type of structure you can build. Today you can even buy concrete logs, which deliver a realistic log look with the protection of stone.

Roof. The roof is the most vulnerable part of your home. Metal, Class A asphalt shingles, slate, clay or terra-cotta tile, cement and concrete products are all good fire-resistant choices Shake shingle roofs burn easily, not only because they are wood, but because of all the exposed edges. Even worse, shake shingles turn into missiles in a wind-driven firestorm, and start spot fires wherever they land. In many wildland places traditional shake shingle roofs are now illegal.

Multi-faceted roofs are all the design rage, but when it comes to fire safety, simple is better. A roof design with no valleys is best, because heat can pool in any type of depression, creating eddies and hot spots that can eventually start the roof on fire.

Windows. Who doesn't want a wall of windows to show off all those fabulous views, or just to watch the wildlife and enjoy being surrounded by Mother Nature? Unfortunately the bigger the windows, the more vulnerable they are to breaking in the intense heat from a fire and letting in flames. Smaller windows hold up better in their frames. Choose double- or triple-paned windows or tempered glass. Avoid plastic skylights; they can easily melt and let in a firestorm.

Doors. Use solid-core exterior doors no less than 1¾-inch thick, with good weather stripping. Put in a self-closing door with a tight seal between the house and the garage. It's usually tougher to completely seal garage doors, so make sure if something in the garage catches fire, you can keep flames from getting into the house.

Escape Routes. Experts recommend that every room have at least two escape routes (for example one window and one door, or two windows.) Plus you should have at least two solid ground-level doors to the outside. Be sure you also have a safe way to get to your vehicles.

Shutters. Non-flammable shutters on windows and skylights can help keep fire on the outside from getting in.

Vents & Eaves. Vents are very vulnerable to flying embers. Box in eaves, fascias, soffits and vents or enclose them with 1/8-inch metal mesh. Don't use plastic or fiberglass; both will melt and burn. Attic vents in eaves and cornices also need to be baffled or otherwise protected.

Chimneys. Chimneys need to be equipped with spark arresters and screens that prevent embers from dropping into your home (and will also keep sparks from the chimney from getting out...and birds from flying in).

Decks, Porches and Outdoor Living Spaces. Our decks and patios combined had almost as many square feet as our house. Your decks, porches, balconies and attached garage should be treated as if they are part of your house; calculate defensible space from their outer boundaries.

Decks present special hazards in wildfires; they can heat from underneath and eventually ignite from radiant or convective heat, and flying embers can pile up on the top surface of a deck, creating a sort of fire sandwich. Redwood and cedar decks look great and stand up to moisture, bugs and rot, but they will burn, as will lumber treated to be fire-resistant. Composition decks are harder to catch on fire, but once they get going they burn like a really big candle. LEED-certified fireproof decking is now available from Lifetime Lumber, and undoubtedly other sources. Deck supports should be treated and coated; they are usually slower to catch on fire than the deck itself because they are thicker. Wooden decks should be made of material that is at least three inches thick.

Don't plan on storing anything that can burn under your deck, such as firewood, deck furniture, tarps, recycling, wooden canoes, etc. Metal screening of 1/8-inch or smaller between the outside bottom edge of the deck and the ground will keep embers from blowing under your deck, and also keep out debris, leaves, twigs and critters.

Stone sometimes explodes or pulverizes, but it doesn't readily burn. Cladding your support posts and your foundation in stonework helps provide a barrier for ground-burning fires. If the posts go right into the ground, add an area of gravel or stone all the way around. Stone patios and gravel mulch can add to your defensibility

Water Sources and Storage. Wildland fire experts advise that people living in areas without fire hydrants or an easily accessible nearby year-round water source like a reservoir or lake have a community water storage tank. If that's not possible or practical, allow for at least a 2,500 gallon storage tank on site.

Retrofitting Your Home

What if you already own a home that you now realize has some fire-vulnerable design and construction features that are impossible or cost prohibitive to change? There are still many steps you can take to improve your ability to withstand a wildfire. Doing anything is better than doing nothing.

Since the **roof** is the most vulnerable part of a home or outbuilding, having a fire-resistant one (Class A) should be a high priority. Replacing a roof is expensive, but many insurance companies offer substantial discounts for hazard-resistant roofs, so check with them first to get a list of brands and types that qualify.

Replacing single-paned **windows** with double-paned or tempered glass will give your home an extra layer of protection and save energy as well. Screens should have metal frames as well as metal—not plastic—mesh.

To keep firebrands out, use 1/8-inch metal mesh to screen under **decks, enclose foundations, and enclose eaves and vents.**

Screen your **chimney** opening and install a spark arrester that meets National Fire Protection Association Standard 211.

Check for places where combustible materials meet each other, providing **a pathway for fire**, such as a wooden fence attached to wooden stairs leading to a wooden deck, and separate them with a span of non-flammable material, if you can.

Store boats, campers, lawnmowers and recreational vehicles that contain gasoline in a building or well away from your home.

For extra safety, consider metal or all-weather (the latest designer name for fancy faux woods and wickers) **outdoor furniture**. It may not survive (ours didn't), but it won't add any fuel to the fire. Door mats, furniture cushions and covers, planters and window boxes all provide good places

Two examples of what **not** to do when living in the WUI.

for embers to smolder. Rubber mats, flame-retardant furniture covers and metal, cement or pottery planters are a better choice.

Ongoing Maintenance

- Regularly clean your roof and gutters; don't allow debris to pile up anywhere. Repair any breaks between tiles where debris could hide.
- Patrol your defensible space and remove downed tree branches, trash and debris that could ignite.
- Clean chimneys at least once a year if you use your fireplace regularly; more often if you heat with wood or use your fireplace a lot.
- Don't pile firewood on or under your deck or up against your house. Store firewood down from prevailing winds and a minimum of 30 feet away from your house or any outbuildings.
- Keep your grass and weeds trimmed. Dispose of cuttings and debris before they have a chance to turn into tinder.
- Thin trees and brush; remove branches overhanging chimney and roof.
- Keep plants and bushes well-watered. Remove any dead plant materials immediately. Natural mulches like wood chips and bark turn into kindling when they are dry; gravel or rock mulch is a better insulator for plants and provides a fire break instead of a source of fuel. And rock mulch never blows away.
- Clear vegetation around cisterns, propane tanks and fire hydrants.
- Make sure address signs are clearly visible from the access road.

Handling the Little Unexpected Emergencies

You can't fight a raging wildfire. But everyone who lives in the WUI should be prepared to handle life's unexpected little emergencies.

When we first moved in our fire pit was off our back deck; our woodpile was perhaps 25 feet downhill under a big ponderosa pine. One night we had a fire in the fire pit; we were sure it was out when we went to bed. The next morning my husband Cory went to town to run some errands. I was still in my polar fleece robe in my office when I looked out the window and saw flames shooting up into a big tree. I ran outside in my slippers and grabbed the water bucket we kept nearby, which had all the effect of throwing a teacup of water on a bonfire. Somehow I had the presence of mind to call my nearest neighbor and 911; then I ran back and forth with buckets of water. My neighbor and her kids joined my bucket brigade, and together we kept the fire from spreading until the volunteer fire department showed up to put it out for real. The heat singed off one of my eyebrows, and the sleeves of my robe melted to my arms.

If I had gone to town, our house would have probably burned down that day. We did so many things wrong it's hard to know where to start. Our woodpile should have been uphill and upwind and at least 30 feet away from the house. Our fire should have been stone cold, stick-your-hand-in-it out before we went to bed; having a heavy lid to cover the pit would have been even better. I should have called 911 before I ran outside. And a polyester robe did not make for good fire-fighting gear. We should have had a long hose hooked up, and shovels and rakes handy. We learned a lot that day. When a lightning strike started a small fire near our home a couple of years later, we were much better prepared.

Necessities of Life in the WUI

Smoke Alarms. Install a smoke alarm on each level of your home, especially near bedrooms. While there are still a few states that do not mandate smoke alarms, they do save lives, so install them even if you don't have to. Use long-life batteries, and change them at least once a year. Test alarms monthly. You'll probably smell, hear and see a wildfire long before your smoke alarms go off, but they'll be able to warn you if a fire starts in or around your house.

Fire Extinguishers. Keep a fire extinguisher on every level and in the garage. Make sure everyone knows where they are, and how to use them. It's not as easy as it looks in the movies.

Hand Tools. Assemble rakes, shovels, buckets, and a handsaw or chainsaw, and keep them together in one place. Wildland firefighters use a handy tool called a Pulaski that's part axe and part adze; it can both dig and chop. Firefighters use their Pulaskis to construct fire line, but it's also a handy tool for homeowners who have to dig holes in hard-packed soil or clay or areas full of roots and stones. And it won't run out of gas until you do.

Hoses, Buckets and Ladders. Have a hose hooked up and ready to use by all of your outdoor faucets. It's good to have freeze-proof exterior water outlets on at least two sides of your home. Ladders and buckets are just necessities of life in the WUI.

Can Responders Find and Reach You?

Emergency services can't save you if they can't find you or reach you. Mark your address in a way that's easily identifiable from the main access road, and again on your home. Fancy script numbers carved into a rock may look great, but they do no good if no one can read them. This is one area where it's worth sacrificing aesthetics for real-world performance. Put up big house numbers that can be read from a distance and are reflective, lit by solar-powered lights or glow in the dark. Don't make firefighters sacrifice precious time trying to find your home, or even worse, drive by without realizing anyone is there.

Locked gates can present a host of problems that can delay emergency responders. A simple chain lock or padlock can easily be removed, but heavy duty electronic gates and walls and metal fences can keep out more than trespassers. If your property access is gated or you live in a gated community, it's imperative that you give your gate access code to emergency dispatch and the local fire department, and notify them when you change it.

There are also a wide range of entry options for providing emergency responders with quick access, from special keyed locks to audio activation that recognizes the specific siren frequency of ambulances and fire trucks and prompts the gate to open. There are also radio-controlled options that allow responders who arrive in personal vehicles to gain access. Many counties are now passing standards requiring new developments to install gates with fail-safes that allow emergency service officials to gain entry without an access code.

CHAPTER 4

Defensible Space You Can Live With

Defensible space is just what it sounds like. It's the area surrounding your home where you've taken steps to reduce both natural and man-made wildfire hazards so a fire has less fuel to burn. That reduces both the speed and intensity of an approaching wildfire. Defensible space also gives firefighters room to work safely if they are able to try to defend your home. And good defensible space combined with Firewise construction and maintenance helps your home defend itself.

When we discovered that both the home we were building and the defensible space we created would have to pass a fire-safety inspection before we could move in, our biggest worry was that "they" would make us cut down our precious trees. We weren't thinking about wildfire risk, or what we could do to improve our home's chance of surviving a wildfire. We were only concerned about having to do something that would interfere with our privacy or detract from the natural beauty.

Many people resist the concept of creating defensible space. The term conjures up a barren landscape of rock and dirt surrounding your home; no trees, no shade, no plants…totally lacking the natural beauty you moved out of the city to enjoy. And many people are convinced that defensible space doesn't work, so why give up anything to create it?

The devastating Fourmile Canyon fire in 2010 just west of Boulder, Colorado destroyed 168 homes and gobbled up 6,200 acres. There were 474 homes within the wildfire's perimeter. Slightly more than 35% of those homes were destroyed, which is a fairly typical percentage in a WUI fire. Of those homes, 29 were ignited by crown fire traveling through the tree tops and 139 by surface fire traveling along the ground. As is typical, most of the homes that were lost burned to the ground in the first 12 hours of the fire.

The official report on the fire concluded that the lack of defensible space within 100 feet of the homes was the primary reason the homes destroyed by surface fire were lost.

But when 127 of the evacuated landowners whose homes survived were surveyed, most of them were in denial. They still did not believe that the characteristics of their home and immediate surroundings would make much difference if another wildfire struck. Little wonder the average homeowner thinks defensible space is just another bureaucratic annoyance designed to interfere with their personal freedom.

There are many studies showing that homes with effective defensible space are much more likely to survive a wildfire; adding a nonflammable roof greatly improves the odds. The infamous Paint Fire in Santa Barbara, California in 1990 destroyed more than 500 homes, but 86% of the homes with nonflammable roofs and at least 60 feet of defensible space (or what Firewise terms a modified landscape) survived.

Nothing you can do will guarantee your home will make it through a wildfire. Under the most extreme conditions, any home can be destroyed. The Crystal Fire that burned our home to the ground was so intensely hot it melted tempered glass, twisted steel I-beams, pulverized our concrete foundation, and destroyed other homes with metal roofs and stucco construction (they burned from the inside out). But what you do before wildfire threatens can dramatically improve the odds that your home will survive.

Defensible space will give your home a much better chance of weathering a wildfire. And defensible space could save your life.

Creating defensible space isn't an option. It's a necessity.

How Much Defensible Space is Enough?

The amount of defensible space depends on a lot of things that are specific to where you live and the topography where your home is situated. Defensible space is generally an area that includes your home and everything around it that's been designed or modified to stop or severely slow down the spread of flames and reduce exposure to radiant heat. This is also sometimes referred to as the Home Ignition Zone.

Firewise research suggests that homes within 100 feet of flames from a canopy fire are in danger of igniting, even if the flames don't come any closer. Defensible space guidelines range from a minimum of 30 feet to a maximum of 200 feet, depending on your location, topography, weather conditions and other factors. California now mandates a minimum of 100 feet of defensible space.

If your home is built in a pine or conifer forest, you need a minimum of 100 feet of defensible space. If your home is built into or sitting on top of a steep slope covered in any kind of flammable vegetation, you are at more risk, because fire generally runs uphill. You will want to talk to an expert about additional steps you can take to protect it.

You don't have to cut down all the trees within 100 feet of your house; if you have big beautiful shade trees you really want to keep, you can incorporate them into your home's footprint and make them part of your defensible space as long as they don't come in contact with or hang over your roof or flammable deck. Then your job is to create an area that extends out around your home and trees that slows down fire and makes it hard for it to spread.

Firewise Landscaping

If you design your landscape with wildfire safety in mind, you can create a beautiful landscape that can help contain fire instead of fuel it. It's all a matter of choosing the right materials, plants, shrubs and trees, then spacing them properly and taking good care of them. You can use driveways, walkways, patios and water features to add interest and reduce fire danger. See your state forest or county website for recommendations on fire-resistant plants that do well in your area. There are also links to local plant lists provided by the Cooperative Extension Services of many states listed on the Firewise website.

A wide, mowed perimeter helped keep the wildfire away from this home.

The Fire-Free Five saved this Texas home.

It's important to maintain your landscape to keep it in fire-resistant condition. That means pruning, weeding, mowing, trimming dead branches and removing dead and dried plants. If water—or the lack thereof—is a perennial issue, consider using non-woody native plants that require little irrigation, and incorporating features like walkways, patios, stone walls and boulderscapes that need little care and actually improve your defensibility.

Maintenance is an ongoing process. Something as seemingly innocent as a forgotten basket of clippings that have dried out in the sun or wheelbarrow of firewood left too close to the house can turn into a deadly ignition source in seconds.

Upwards of a quarter of the homes built in the WUI are second homes. If yours is one of them and you don't have someone regularly doing maintenance, err on the side of too much defensible space, and make your ignition zone as maintenance free and spark-proof as you possibly can.

Zone One: 0 to 30 Feet (for all homes in the WUI)

Zone One is typically defined as 30 feet in all directions from your house and any attached structures such as decks, garages and storage buildings, as well as any trees next to the house you are incorporating into your defensible space. Experts recommend that everyone in the WUI create a Firewise Zone 1 regardless of your hazard-area rating.

Fire-Free Five. Make a minimum of the first five feet surrounding your house totally free of anything flammable. Use fire-resistant landscaping materials such as rock mulch (bark and chip mulch become flammable when dry) or stone walkways, or plant high moisture content annuals or perennials.

Five to 30 feet. Choose plants that are low growing and don't contain waxes, resins and oils that burn easily. Group and space plantings so they don't create a continuous path for the fire.

- Trim tree branches that overhang the house.
- Trim trees branches up 6 to 10 feet from the ground; this prevents the lower branches from serving as ladders for the fire to climb.
- Space conifer trees so there is 30 feet between crowns. If you plan to cut down trees around your home to improve your defensible space choose wisely: conifers, pines, evergreens, firs and eucalyptus will catch on fire faster than hardwood trees.
- Keep your grass watered and mowed. A well-watered lawn can serve as a fire break. A dry, overgrown lawn can serve as a fire path. If you live in an arid climate or have to deal with frequent water restrictions, consider xeriscaping with rock and fire-resistant, drought-tolerant plants and groundcovers.
- Remove any dead vegetation from under decks and within ten feet of the house. Once you've screened in the space below your deck, you'll have an easier time keeping blowing leaves and debris out. But it will probably still pile up when the wind blows, so make a habit of walking your perimeter regularly during fire season.
- Locate propane tanks and woodpiles outside this zone.

Zone One (the first 30 feet) applies to all homes in the WUI. Zone Two (30 to 100 feet) applies to homes in moderate- to high-hazard areas. Zone Three (100 to 200 feet) is for high hazard areas. *Courtesy of the NFPA Firewise Communities Program*

Zone Two: 30 to 100 Feet (for Moderate and High Hazard Areas)

- Use plantings that are low-growing, well-irrigated and less flammable.
- Trees should be clustered in groups of two or three with 30 feet between clusters; leave 20 feet between individual trees.
- Prune lower branches up 6 to 10 feet from the ground.
- Encourage a mix of deciduous and coniferous trees if your climate permits.
- Create fire breaks with walkways, lawns, water features, rock gardens, rock patios and gravel or paved driveways.

Zone Three: 100 to 200 Feet (for High Hazard Areas)

Reduce density in this area by thinning and creating more space between trees. Prune tall trees so the crowns (tops) don't touch. Remove small conifers growing in between larger trees—they provide ladder fuel.

If you have several acres or more, you might want to consult a forester about the smartest way to thin. Some studies show that thinning for thinning's sake can actually make it easier for a surface fire to spread. The best approach is to execute a plan that takes typical fire behavior during dry and windy conditions into account rather than just thin to an arbitrary density.

....

What To Do with Slash Piles

Mounds of tree branches and debris are the inevitable result of thinning or removing dead or diseased trees. Slash piles can turn into gigantic fire-feeding bonfires if a wildfire sweeps through, so before you start cutting, figure out what you're going to do with your slash. Some communities have chipping programs, where you can take slash to a central collection site. Some landfills and recycling yards accept slash. You can buy a chipper that will take care of small and medium sized branches. And in many places you can rent an industrial-strength chipper that will chew up just about anything; perhaps your neighbors or association will share the cost. Now all you have to do is figure out what to do with all that mulch; just don't spread it around your house. Often burning slash is prohibited during fire season, and regulated the rest of the year, along with other types of open burning. Check with your county so you understand local regulations and get the required permits.

....

CHAPTER 5

A Homeowner's Guide to Insurance

Have you actually read your homeowner's insurance policy? If your answer is a resounding NO, then you are not alone. Most people consider home insurance something you have to have, but will use only occasionally, if ever. And they trust that their insurance company will be there when they need them.

You've probably glanced at your renewal letter each year, grumbled if your premiums have gone up, and promised yourself that this year you're going to go over your coverage with your agent. Next thing you know it's Christmas and another year has slipped away. So it goes on the list for next year. But sometimes next year is too late.

Few people buy insurance planning to use it someday to replace their home and everything they owned. No one really believes they'll have to deal with the worst case scenario, because "what are the chances of that happening?"

But if the worst case scenario is the one you're facing, your insurance will become your lifeline to recovery. There's nothing worse than sitting down with your adjustor and finding out that you are underinsured, under-documented and unprepared to go through the lengthy process of substantiating your claim and collecting what you are due.

So if it's been a while since you've even talked to your agent, make an appointment now. The first review will be the hardest. After that it will get easier. Some policies have an automatic inflation clause that increases your coverage each year based on the national inflation index; that might account for normal inflation, but it won't account for improvements you've made to your home or changes in local conditions. You should review your coverage annually.

Are You Underinsured?

In the average wildfire, more than half of the people who lose their home are underinsured by 25% or more. When you suffer a total loss that runs into hundreds of thousands of dollars, that's a lot of money.

Why are people underinsured? Often it's because the amount of insurance people initially take out is based on covering the mortgage or market value. They are focused on making the bank happy and keeping the monthly payment as low as possible, so they accept the insurance company's initial recommendation and cross "buy homeowner's insurance" off the to-do list. Or they don't think about how much it would really cost to rebuild their home and replace all their belongings. Disasters are terrible things that happen to *other* people.

Housing values plummeted in many parts of the country during the recent economic downturn, now being referred to as the Great Recession, and may take many years to recover. But the cost to build has continued to climb, creating a wider and wider gap between market value and actual replacement cost. And in a widespread disaster, local supply and demand issues often cause building costs to balloon even further. You'll shortchange yourself if you base your insurance on market value, even if you think that you would buy another home rather than rebuild.

True replacement cost for a home is also a very individual matter. When insurance companies are calculating average replacement cost, they use square-foot tables and software programs that are generally based on average new construction. Your home might have custom or unusual features, higher quality materials and other features that won't be taken into consideration unless you bring them up, like your quarry tile floors, wall-to-wall two-story stone fireplace, or wrap-around deck. Or you may have built your home in an area where materials and equipment have to be hauled long distances over rough roads, routinely adding to building costs.

Another reason for being underinsured is that homes seldom remain "as is." People do lots of homework, but forget to turn it in for extra credit. People remodel kitchens and baths, upgrade flooring, replace windows, doors and even the roof, add decks, patios and water features. They make additions and build outbuildings. They upgrade lighting and built-in appliances, and trade in the standard countertops for granite. People do all kinds of things that increase the value of their home, but they seldom think about reporting them to their insurance company and adjusting their coverage. Most policies specify that you need to notify your carrier about any improvements you make that add more than $5,000 to the value of your home within 90 days.

Sometimes people know they are underinsured, but are trying to keep their premiums as low as possible, and figure some coverage is better than no coverage. Or they're willing to roll the dice and play the odds and cross their fingers. I can only tell you from talking to hundreds of survivors that nobody feels that way after their home burns down and they're faced with the emotionally draining and incredibly expensive task of starting over. I've never talked with anyone who said, "Gee, I wish we'd had less insurance."

Only 4% of homeowners are completely uninsured, according to the Insurance Research Council. If you live in wildfire country, don't be one of them. There are hundreds of property and casualty insurance companies licensed in most states; if one turns you down, find out why; there may be things you can do to increase your insurability. Asking your neighbors is a good way to find carriers who are issuing policies where you live. Or consult an independent insurance broker who represents multiple companies. You can also visit *www.insureme.com* for quotes and rates.

Does your policy cover the high cost of cleanup and the removal of debris, which counties often require be handled as hazardous waste?

Your Basic Homeowner's Policy

The typical homeowner's insurance policy covers damage to your home and your belongings resulting from fire, windstorm, hail, water damage (excluding flooding), riots and explosions as well as other causes of loss, such as theft. Many, but not all, policies cover the extra cost of living somewhere else while your home is being repaired or rebuilt, or while you are finding a new one.

The amount of coverage you have for your home and the various schedules and endorsements should be on the face or cover page of your policy, often referred to as the declarations (DEC) page; any riders and endorsements should also be listed. Reading your cover page is a good place to start.

Here are the various standard schedules included in most policies; percentages covered and terms of that coverage vary by carrier, so be sure to read your policy and go over the provisions with your agent.

Coverage A – Dwelling. Covers your home and structures attached to it, such as attached garages and decks. For insurance purposes, your dwelling includes everything in your house that wouldn't fall out if you turned it upside down.

Coverage B – Other Structures. Typically a percentage of Coverage A that covers structures that aren't attached to your house, such as a detached garage, shop, barn or storage building; 10% of your dwelling coverage is common. Any personal property inside the structure is covered under your Coverage C (personal property).

Coverage C – Unscheduled Personal Property. Covers all the personal property inside and outside your home—all that stuff that would fall out if you turned your house upside down; 70% of your dwelling coverage is typical, but percentages vary.

Coverage D – Loss of Use. Provides additional living expenses (ALE) that reimburse you for expenses above and beyond the ordinary if you can't stay in your home due to an event (like a wildfire) that is covered by your policy. ALE can provide coverage for a specified amount of time, generally one to two years, or a flat dollar amount.

Coverage E – Personal Liability. Provides coverage if someone sues you or files a claim against you for bodily injury and/or damage resulting from negligence on your property, like stepping into a burning stump hole.

Coverage F – Medical Payments. Provides coverage for medical payments if a third party is injured by or on your property.

Scheduled Personal Property. In a typical homeowner's policy, there are set dollar limits for certain types of personal property: firearms, art, jewelry, cash and negotiable securities, computers and similar types of media equipment, business equipment, etc. Read your policy to see what these limits are. Policy limits for most of these items don't apply in case of a total loss. However, if you have any riders on your policy or additional floater policies that provide extra coverage for these types of items, that amount will be in addition to your personal property Schedule C coverage.

Landscaping and Trees. Coverage for landscaping and trees is typically a percentage of your dwelling amount, although loss per individual tree is limited by a dollar amount; 5% is typical.

Replacement Cost vs. Actual Cash Value

Replacement cost (RC) means that your policy will pay for the actual cost to replace an item at today's prices, no matter how you got the item, what condition it was in, or what you paid for it, if anything. You are initially paid for the actual cash value at time of loss for your property, sometimes also called depreciated value. Then when you replace the property, you are paid the difference between actual cash or depreciated value and what it cost to replace the item with the same or similar one.

Actual cash value (ACV), sometimes also called fair market value, is what your home or property would sell for on the open market at the time of loss. For things like antiques, artwork and other items that tend to increase in value over time, cash value could be the same as replacement cost. But for most of the things you own, cash value will only be a fraction of what it will actually cost to replace the item. Most newer home insurance policies from well-rated companies are for replacement value, but don't take that for granted; read your policy and ask your agent. If replacement value isn't spelled out in your policy, your coverage is only for actual cash value.

For example, a big screen TV that cost $3,000 has an expected life of ten years. If the TV is five years old when your house burns down, and you have a cash-value policy, you'll get paid $1,500. If you have replacement value, you'll be paid the depreciated value ($1,500) up front. When you replace the TV and submit a receipt, you'll be paid the rest, up to the actual replacement cost for the same make and model.

Extended Replacement Cost Coverage

Many insurance policies provide for additional replacement costs for your home itself above and beyond the face amount of your coverage. An additional 10% to 30% is common; extended coverage of an additional 50% or more is available from a few high-end carriers.

How does extended replacement cost work? If your basic dwelling coverage is $200,000 and your policy provides for 120% of replacement value for your dwelling, you'd be able to collect up to $240,000 to rebuild your home on your property, build elsewhere or buy another home, assuming the estimate to replace the house you lost is at least $240,000.

Extended replacement cost doesn't usually apply to personal property or other structures or covered losses. Having extended replacement cost coverage in your policy can make a huge difference in helping you build or buy a home that's more comparable to the one you lost.

Valued Policy Laws

Eighteen states have some version of valued policy law that requires insurance companies to pay out the policy limits without requiring any further proof of value in the event of a total covered loss. In most of these states valued policy laws apply only to your personal home, not to the contents or to rental property. In some states, insurance companies can deduct depreciation that occurs after the policy was written. The definition of total loss is subject to interpretation; if any part of the structure can be used, like the foundation, it's generally not considered a total loss. The rules, regulations and provisions vary widely from state to state. If you live in a wildfire-risk area in a valued policy state, have a long talk with your insurance agent and make sure you completely understand what will happen and what you will be able to collect if your house burns down.

The states with some form of valued policy law are Arkansas, Florida, Georgia, Kansas, Louisiana, Minnesota, Mississippi, Missouri, Montana, Nebraska, New Hampshire, North Dakota, Ohio, South Carolina, South Dakota, Tennessee, Texas, West Virginia and Wisconsin.

Land and Improvements

Homeowner's insurance does not cover land (other than a percentage for landscaping) or infrastructure like private roads, wells, septic fields, utilities, and phone lines. If your infrastructure is destroyed in a fire and you rebuild— or if you buy unimproved property and build elsewhere—you will have to come up with the money for this infrastructure. If your home burns down, you will still own your land.

Determining the Coverage You Need

If you just finished building your home from the ground up, you may have a good idea of how much it would cost to replace it. But if you bought an existing home, or built your home more than a few years ago, how do you find out how much it would cost to build it today?

Experts recommend that you get estimates from at least two local general contractors so you can accurately answer that question. You may be able to get a ballpark per square foot estimate for free, but you will most likely have to pay for a detailed estimate. Independent assessors will do the job for a fee, usually between $250 and $500.

A good insurance agent can work you through a questionnaire designed to ferret out all the features that go into determining your actual replacement cost. There are also several websites you can use to create an insurable valuation report for a modest fee (generally under $10). Three well-recommended sites are HMFacts *(www.hmfacts.com)*, AccuCoverage *(www.accucoverage.com)*, and Insure to Value *(www.bluebook.net/products/insure-to-value/).*

Using the interactive software on these websites, it should take you less than an hour to enter your information once you have it organized. You'll need your total square feet of living space, including your basement, number of bedrooms, bathrooms, construction materials, types of finishes (granite, Formica etc.), floor coverings, wall coverings, etc. You will still need to factor in any extraordinary features that no software is smart enough to know about, like your hand-troweled walls or tin ceiling, as well as the additional cost of labor for any special custom features.

When our adjustor reconstructed our home on paper after the fire, we were astonished to find out that despite the depressed real estate market, our ten-year-old log home would now cost over twice as much to rebuild as it cost us to build in the first place.

We'd made an all too common mistake; we'd neglected to take into account the added cost of all the improvements and upgrades we'd made over the years as well as the general escalation in building costs. We hadn't been intentionally hiding anything from our insurance company or trying to cut our premiums; we just hadn't thought about the fact that our new bathrooms, upgraded kitchen counters and expanded deck, pond and patio all added to the replacement cost of our home.

As a result, we ended up having our dwelling, as your policy refers to your home, underinsured. And because the amounts you can be reimbursed for your personal property, outbuildings, landscaping and debris removal are all percentages of your basic dwelling coverage, having your home underinsured affects the maximum amount of money you can collect for everything else as well.

Coverage for Building Code Compliance and Code Upgrades

The older your home is, the more important it is to have coverage for building code upgrades and compliance, commonly known as Ordinance and Law (OAL). Some policies provide a percentage, typically 10% of your dwelling coverage; others specify a flat amount. The cost of complying with code upgrades can be astronomical, especially if major features of your former home would no longer be to code. Since your policy pays to rebuild your home as it existed at the time of the fire, you need code compliance coverage to pay for necessary upgrades. This coverage will also cover the costs of building permits.

Debris Removal and Cleanup Coverage

It's hard enough to swallow the fact that your beautiful home is now regarded as debris to be loaded into giant "burrito bags" and hauled away to the landfill. Even worse is the fact that debris removal and site cleanup can be extremely expensive, and methods of debris disposal are generally dictated by the county or state. In some areas homes built before the mid-1980s are automatically treated as hazardous waste, which makes the debris removal process even more expensive. If you can document that no asbestos was used in your home, put the info in your house file. Read your policy and make sure debris removal is covered. It's usually a percentage of your Coverage A, or dwelling amount. The debris removal for the cremains of our 3,500-plus square-foot log home was within our coverage limits ($20,000), but I have talked to people with similar debris situations who had to spend over $50,000 to have their debris removed and disposed of according to their county's regulations.

Additional Living Expenses (ALE)

Additional living expenses can include everything from the cost of rental housing for your family to boarding for pets or livestock. The timeframe covered varies by insurance company, generally between one and two years. Experts caution that one year may not be enough, particularly if you plan to rebuild. Some insurance companies will extend the time frame that they'll cover additional living expenses if you are rebuilding, especially in cases where there has been a big disaster with widespread losses, and not everyone can rebuild at once. It's use-it-or-lose-it coverage; if you don't use your ALE coverage, you don't get to collect the money that would've been available.

Our policy provided for up to two years' worth of additional living expenses, and our insurance company covered the cost of an extended-living motel while they found us a suitable home to rent. Some insurance companies expect you to find your own housing, and to rent or buy furniture and other necessities.

If you have ALE, your insurance company is required to provide you comparable living. If you had a four-bedroom home on 40 acres in the mountains, you would be able to rent a similar home to live in, if you wanted to.

Additional living expenses will also come into play if your home is damaged to the extent that it is uninhabitable while it's being repaired.

Even if your home is not damaged or destroyed, as long as you were officially evacuated and were unable to stay in your home, additional living expenses can be covered. In this case, ALE may be subject to your deductible and/or limited to two weeks, regardless of how long you are actually evacuated. Read your policy and check with your agent to be sure.

Ten Questions to Ask Your Insurance Agent

1) How much is my house insured for? How was that amount of coverage determined? If my home was destroyed today, how much would it be depreciated? Do I have the best policy available?
2) Does my policy cover Replacement Value for my home and personal property?
3) Does my policy cover Additional Living Expenses? For how long? (Or how much, if it's a set dollar amount?)
4) Do I have Extended Replacement coverage? How much? Does it apply to anything besides my house?
5) How much coverage do I have for my detached garage, shop, and other outbuildings and landscaping?
6) Does my policy cover the increased cost of upgrades dictated by changes in building codes or laws (Ordinance and Law coverage), and how much?
7) What does my policy cover if I'm officially evacuated for a fire or any other reason? Do I need to pay the deductible?
8) Does my policy cover debris removal? How much?
9) What's my deductible? How much would I save if I increased it?
10) Are there any available discounts I could qualify for? Is there anything else I can do to decrease my premium?

Rate Your Carrier

Insurance companies are rated by Standard & Poors for their financial strength. Ratings of A or above are best, and are easy to find on *www.insure. com*. The ratings will also show you if a particular carrier is under regulatory supervision, or likely to experience difficulties paying claims in certain situations. You can also review customer satisfaction ratings for many companies based on consumer surveys conducted by *www.insure.com*. *Consumer Reports* also periodically rates insurance companies on several different factors.

When Policy Limits Don't Apply

If your home is a total loss, policy limits for many types of property do not apply. You should be able to claim your full loss for art, jewelry, antiques, firearms, etc., whether or not you had a rider or floater policy. If you have a rider or floater, it will add to your total coverage for personal property. If you don't, the total loss will count toward your personal property inventory.

Example: Assume your personal property coverage (Schedule C) is $100,000. You added a rider that covers some of your jewelry for $10,000. If the covered jewelry was lost in the fire, you can potentially collect $110,000. If you don't have a rider, your $10,000 worth of jewelry becomes line items on your inventory that you will need to document piece by piece. But it can be claimed in full, even if your limit for jewelry would have been $1,500 if your home had been burglarized instead of destroyed.

Exceptions to the no-limits rule include cash, negotiable securities, and business equipment, which all typically still have modest limits. Imagine how easy it would be to claim you had a million bucks stashed under your bed. Business property generally needs to be covered separately. If you run a business out of your home, talk to your agent and your accountant about business coverage.

Tips for Reducing Your Premium

Without insurance you'll shoulder the total burden of rebuilding or buying another home, and replacing all of your possessions. Statistically speaking, it's unlikely your home will burn down in a wildfire. But rolling the dice puts your family's entire future at risk. Check out these tips for reducing your premium, and get quotes from several companies so you can compare coverage and rates. A recent study from Yale University showed that insurance premiums for essentially the same coverage vary by carrier much more than you might think.

Increase Your Deductible. Think of your homeowner's insurance as major medical coverage for your home. Opting for a higher deductible can save you 25% or more annually. And having a higher deductible will also keep you from filing small claims, which can give your insurance company cause to raise your premium or decline to renew your policy. Studies from *Consumer Reports* show that having a higher deductible saves money over time and preserves your insurance for when it's really needed.

Don't File Small Claims. Claims from all insurance companies go into a national database; on average people file one claim every ten years. All insurance companies use that database. Pile up too many claims in too short a time and you become a poor risk. That makes it harder for you to get good insurance, and makes your policy more expensive.

Bundle Coverage. If you can use one company for all your insurance needs, you can save money. Bundling your coverage for your cars, life insurance and property can result in savings of 5% to 15% on all policies.

Ask About Discounts. Ask upfront about anything you can do that would reduce your premium. There may be discounts available for:

- Smoke detectors
- Fire extinguishers
- Sprinkler systems
- Burglar and fire alarms that alert an outside service
- Deadbolt locks and fire-safe window grates
- Being 55 years old and/or retired
- Long-time policyholder
- Claim-free history
- Upgrades to plumbing, heating and electrical systems
- Retrofitting that makes your home more fireproof
- Wind-resistant shutters
- Fire-rated roof
- Living within 5 miles of a fire station
- On-site water storage
- Firewise mitigation

Comparison Shop

Insurance policies vary widely, as do premiums. Some companies offer Cadillacs; others offer economy cars that save you money every year, but may not cover as much if you need to use your policy. Some trade-outs may be worth it based on your circumstances; some may not.

It's pretty easy to compare premiums; there are even several sites on the Internet that let you comparison shop for policies. NetQuote *(www. netquote.com)* is considered a reliable one. However it's incredibly hard to do a side-by-side analysis of coverage and policies. So hard in fact that a recent research study from the University of Minnesota showed that it is virtually impossible for the average person to accurately compare insurance policies before buying one. Most insurance companies won't send you a policy to review until you've bought insurance. And policies vary much more than you might assume. Even if you could get three companies to give you a copy of their policy before you bought, would you really take the time to read through 150 pages of insurance-speak noting similarities and differences between the companies?

But what's covered and what's not covered will make a huge difference if your home burns down. So you really need to make it a priority to understand what's in your policy and what it really means. That way if you discover your coverage isn't adequate, you need to add business insurance, or you don't have the right policy, you can do something about it now, while you can still make sure you have the coverage you need "just in case."

Rebuild, Build, Buy, Cash Out?

People often assume they must rebuild their home in order to collect their insurance, but usually that is not the case. When you go over your policy with your agent, ask him/her to clearly explain your options. Typically you have the option of rebuilding on site, building somewhere else in the U.S., buying another home, or simply collecting the money you are owed based on your dwelling coverage and established value without having to build or buy. It's important to understand your options and how your choices could affect your total payouts.

Ask your agent if you will be able to collect the extended replacement coverage portion of your policy if you buy another home. Many policies, but not all, have this provision, although because insurance covers your dwelling and other property but not your land, you must exclude the value of your new land. This generally requires you to find several similar-size plots of vacant land in a similar area you can use for comparison.

For example, assume the extended replacement coverage for your home is $400,000, and the new home you want to buy is $440,000. Your search for comps shows the land your new home is situated on is worth $60,000. Your policy would pay $440,000 less $60,000 for the land, or a total of $380,000 up front. To collect the $20,000 that remains of your extended replacement coverage, you would need to make improvements to your new home that make it more comparable to your original home. We replaced the old shake-shingle roof with a Class 4 hail-rated roof on our 'new' home.

Taking the time to understand what your policy does and does not cover and what your options are now will help you make sure you have the coverage that's right for you. And you'll understand your policy if you ever need to use it.

Note: For more information on understanding how insurance works and determining the value of your personal property, see chapter 13.

· ·

Renter's Insurance

According to the Insurance Research Council, 57% of renters have no coverage for their belongings. Why? Renters either think their landlord's insurance covers them or they underestimate the value of everything they own. The landlord's insurance generally covers only the building or home itself, not the tenant's property. And as anyone who has ever had to do a home inventory can tell you, your stuff costs a lot more to replace than you think. Renter's insurance is very affordable; good coverage can be had for less than a dollar a day. In fact, the average renter's insurance premium is under $200 a year. Policy features are similar to homeowner's insurance policies in many ways, providing coverage for additional living expenses, replacement cost for your belongings, and liability coverage.

Thirteen homes burned down in the fire that destroyed our home; three of them were inhabited by renters. None of the tenants had renters' insurance. Starting over from scratch can be financially and emotionally devastating. Why risk your future for a dollar a day? Talk to your insurance agent or visit *www.insureme.com* for lots of information on what to look for and what's covered as well as rate quotes from a range of companies.

· ·

CHAPTER 6

Preparing Your Family for Disaster

Document Your Belongings and Structures

Even if you suffer a total loss, in most cases you'll have to provide your insurance company with a detailed inventory of everything that was destroyed before you'll be able to collect. It's much harder than you might think to remember every single thing you owned, especially at a time when your brain is not firing on all cylinders. If you want to find out just how hard, sit down right now (no peeking) and try to list all your jewelry or tools or everything in just one kitchen drawer.

All those little things really add up. When I inventoried the contents of the pen and pencil mug that had been on my desk, it added up to an astounding $496; it was a McCoy smiley face pottery mug from the 1960s (replacement value: $36), filled with Sharpies and gel pens, a couple of cool old fountain pens ($125 each), a sterling silver letter opener that was a gift from a client ($110), three highlighters, an exacto, a pair of Fiskar scissors, and a pair of good reading glasses. And I probably forgot a couple of things that were in there.

Just about everyone from insurance companies to state and federal agencies recommends you create a room-by-room inventory of everything in your house. There are several free software programs and mobile apps (see the appendix) that will walk you through the process and produce an electronic inventory you can then update as needed. A well-recommended one is *www.knowyourstuff.org* from the Insurance Information Institute. Many states have sample home inventory forms on their state insurance, wildfire or disaster Web pages as well, as do some insurance companies. You may want to look at several options and decide what would work best for you.

If you're overwhelmed by the job, take it one room at a time. It took us about 250 hours to create our inventory after the fire; it ran to 168 pages and 2,500 items and could have gone on for much longer; we quit when we were enough over our maximum to be pretty sure we'd be able to collect our policy limits. Maybe we had more stuff than most people, but having more than 2,000 items on your inventory is common. But I'm sure it would have gone a lot faster if we'd been able to walk through our house, see all of our stuff and use all of our files and records.

Another Approach to Inventory

Not everyone is going to take the time to create and maintain a whole house inventory. But anyone can go through their home room by room, take photos, and put them on a flash drive. Or do a video documentation, and add narrative as you go. Open all your drawers, cupboards and closets. Take photos one section of a room at a time. Take closeups of things like jewelry (even costume), art and collectibles. Photograph your floors, windows, ceilings and moldings. Don't forget bathrooms, storage rooms, laundry room, the giant closet full of Christmas stuff, the attic and basement.

Do the same thing in the garage. Include built-in shelving, garage door openers, tools, yard and lawn equipment, sports equipment and everything else out there. For many people the garage is so full of stuff the cars end up in the driveway.

Go outside and take photos of your home from all angles. Photograph any outbuildings, barns, sheds, fences, patios, decks, ponds, corrals, gardens and any other man-made features of your landscape. Include all your outside furniture and equipment. Open doors and take photos of what's inside your outbuildings. To this day my husband and I wonder what was in three big unmarked cardboard boxes in our storage shed.

Most people can create a thorough photo or video inventory of their home and possessions in less than a day. I took the 75 photos that we used to substantiate our claim in less than two hours. Having a visual documentary of your home and your stuff will make it infinitely easier for you to remember and be compensated for what you had.

Once you've done it, it's much easier to keep your photo-inventory up to date. Take photos of any big new purchases when you bring them home. Don't forget to thoroughly document any remodeling, upgrades, additions and improvements you make, and notify your insurance company about anything you do that increases the value of your home by more than $5,000 within 90 days of completing the project.

Start a file for receipts for all the big-ticket items you buy that you expect to last for several years: electronics, appliances, furniture, etc. "Big Screen TV" won't cut it with your insurance company; they'll want to know make, model number, year acquired and replacement cost. Multiply that by a couple of thousand items and you get an idea of the job ahead. Keep your file of notes and receipts handy and easy to grab if you have to. Another nifty trick is to keep all your warranties, manuals and guarantees in the file; they typically show the make and model. If you are super-organized, you can staple the receipt to the manual.

When you review your photos, you can make notes to go with them. You can even turn them into a Power Point presentation, and add notes to the slides. Or create an ongoing Word document and then print out a copy for your files.

Photos provide great documentation, or as the insurance companies say, "proof of loss." While we still had to spend many hours documenting our loss, the multitude of photos we'd taken supported our claims, and made it much easier to establish both ownership and value.

Keep Your Inventory Safe

You don't want the only copy of your home inventory to be stored on your home computer, or in your file cabinet. If you're not home when a fire starts, all your hard work could go up in flames. So make one flash drive for your file and send a copy along with your notes to someone who lives somewhere that's not threatened by natural disasters. You can also post your photos to an online storage service. In an extremely hot fire, even fire-proof safes can fail, so keep your information somewhere out of danger.

If you opt for a photo inventory, you may still want to do a more detailed written home inventory for some things, such as electronics, power tools, expensive furniture, antiques, jewelry, art, firearms, collectible books and similar items. Include the item, model number, where and when you acquired it and any appraisals, if you have them. If you need to claim these items, it's not what you paid for them that counts; it's what it costs to replace them. (You did make sure you have replacement cost coverage, right?)

If all this work convinces you that even if you collected your policy limits for your contents you'd come up short, you may want to consider carrying a separate floater policy for high-ticket items or other collections that will give you additional coverage in case of a total loss. Floaters and riders also give you extra coverage for theft and in other partial loss situations where these items would normally be subject to modest policy limits.

Create a Family Disaster Plan

When a wildfire threatens, you could have mere minutes to evacuate. Being given a half-hour or less is common. **So take time now to get mentally and physically prepared.** Do all those things you've been putting off for one reason or another. Make a list, tackle it one item at a time, and don't stop until you've crossed everything off. If disaster strikes, you'll never wonder "what if." You'll know you did everything you could.

You might think you are calm, cool and collected, and would instinctively know what to do if disaster loomed. But almost everyone who has ever had to evacuate for a serious fire threat says that when "maybe someday" becomes "RIGHT NOW," the reality is overwhelming. People freeze. They lose focus. They waste precious minutes trying to figure out what to do. One of our neighbors was so rattled they carefully packed up the kitty litter (along with the kitties), but left their cell phones and computers behind.

So plan now. Make your lists now. Practice now. And hope you never need to find out how cool you are under pressure.

Escape Routes. If you have multiple routes for escape, make sure all the drivers in the family are familiar with them; you might have to drive them in the dark through a blanket of smoke. Or one of the routes may be blocked by the fire.

Communication Plan. Designate a place to meet if everyone isn't together when you evacuate, or if you will be driving out more than one vehicle. Choose somewhere easy to remember and locate, and well away from the wildlands. If you'll be hauling out a stock trailer, take that into consideration when you're deciding where to meet up. Don't rely on your memory. Put an index card with the name, address and phone number of where you plan to meet in each glove compartment, along with information of your emergency contact.

Emergency Contact Person. Pick a contact person well out of any potential fire zone, say Aunt Teri in Cleveland. That way if family members are separated, you'll have someone you can call and report in to. In a wide-spread disaster long distance phone systems are often working fine when local systems are overloaded. And you'll have one good friend or relative who can spread the word that you are okay.

Emergency Evacuation Kit

Think through what every family member, including your pets, would need for at least the first few days if you had to flee your home with just a few minutes' notice. This list will be the basis of your family's Emergency Kit. The sample kit below comes from a combination of emergency prepared-ness services and personal experience. Use it as a good place to start, review it item by item and see what things you might want to add based on your particular circumstances. Some of these items could be packed in advance during fire season and stored in your primary vehicle.

Not everyone has the time, means or storage space to put a full kit together and leave it somewhere easy to grab. So assemble everything you have duplicates of, and put into tote boxes. Tape a list on the top that shows what's in the box. Make another list of what you will still need to gather.

Sample Emergency Kit

- Two-way radios if you will be driving out more than one vehicle; don't count on your cell phones getting reception. Smoke interferes with signals, and circuits are often jammed during a major emergency.
- Bottled water and high-energy snacks. Pack more food and water if the nearest town is a long way away, or access roads could be blocked.
- Three days' worth of pet food; store in plastic bowls with lids and you'll have a way to feed and water your pets. Pet treats and a favorite toy may come in very handy as well.
- Leashes, pet crates or carriers.
- A change of clothes, shoes and socks.
- A jacket, sweater or long-sleeved shirt, ball cap or hat with a brim.
- Blanket or sleeping bag; inflatable pillow, pajamas.
- First aid kit.
- Flashlight and lots of batteries.
- Battery-powered radio.

- Extra set of car keys.
- Wet wipes, sanitary supplies, Kleenex, paper towels.
- Sunglasses, goggles (for high winds/blowing embers).
- Reading glasses.
- Work gloves and bandanas.
- Wool blankets, scarves, hats and gloves (wool is a great insulator).
- Bolt cutters (if there are any gates in your path that might be locked).
- Chainsaw (if trees come down on the road).
- Shovel (in case you get stuck).
- Tool kit plus scissors, multi-tool, notebook and pens, duct tape.
- Any special supplies for infants, kids, elderly, disabled.

Your Important Stuff

Now think about everything you'd need to start putting your life back together if you no longer had a home. This list will be a lot more personal and take longer to think through, but doing it now could be a real life saver later.

Use this starter list of important stuff as a beginning. Add and subtract until you've created your own personal list. Then type it up, print it out on colored paper and post a copy somewhere it will be easy to find. Many of these things are in constant use. You can make gathering them up at a moment's notice easier by establishing central locations for things like phones and chargers. Assigning different family members different categories can help speed things up, but you need a master list, in case not everyone is home. Noting where things are located next to the item will make it easier for everyone to help.

I know from experience that putting together some of this information is time consuming, but having it ready when you really need it can save you so much time and so much stress that it's worth it.

Be Ready to Gather Quickly (a starter list for you to customize)

- Cell phones and chargers.
- Computers, external hard drives and power cords.
- Prescriptions and medications (Ibuprofen is going to come in handy).
- Eyeglasses, reading glasses.
- Purses, wallets, credit/debit cards.

- Cash.
- Hard copies of your phone and email contacts and personal info.
- Important documents: birth certificates, marriage certificates, passports, insurance papers and contact info, household inventory, tax files, school and medical records, military service and discharge papers.
- House plans and home improvements file; closing papers or deed, mortgage information, real estate flyer, floor plans.
- Flash drive with household inventory and photos of your home and personal property.
- Investment files and records.
- Stocks, bonds, coins, gold, silver (note: you might want to haul those off to a safe deposit box now or buy a good fire-proof safe).
- Copies of your credit and debit cards, drivers' licenses, photo IDs and card contact numbers.
- Passwords for online accounts.
- List of service providers along with your account info and their contact numbers: Internet, TV, phone, gas, power, water, newspapers, anyone else who services your home or bills you regularly. (Tip: put a copy of a recent bill from each provider into your file.)

Irreplaceable and Valuable Goods

Close your eyes and imagine that you're sitting in an evacuation center in the clothes you're wearing. You escaped with all the stuff on the lists. But everything else you once owned is gone. Now open your eyes, walk around your home and think about what would leave the biggest holes in your heart. Ask your spouse and kids to do the same. Everyone's lists will be different.

Maybe it's those irreplaceable photos of life before the digital age. Your kids' first school project. Family heirlooms. Handmade things that can never be replaced. Your Mom's cookbook. Your grandmother's cross-stitch sampler. Your Dad's coin collection. A favorite painting. A special piece of jewelry. The hood ornament from your first car. Your love letters. Your childhood teddy bear. That autographed baseball.

Even though I've been through several evacuations, and ultimately lost my home in a wildfire, I won't be able to think of everything that might pertain to your personal situation, and neither will anyone else who makes up these lists.

So gather the family together and take time to really think through "what if?" If your kids are old enough to participate, experts say that letting them take part will make them less fearful, not more fearful. There is nothing worse than being frightened and having no clue about what to do. And you might be surprised at what they consider irreplaceable. You can give each child a color-coded tote box and let them fill it with their own personal treasures.

If some of your "must takes" are not in use every day, consider storing them in a tote box or two so they're easy to grab and load. (Do I sound like I have a tote box fixation? It's because they're easy to pack and stack, and have lids to keep out dust. And they can double as an extra table in your motel room. Collapsible laundry baskets also come in handy.)

Anything you can do to put your escape on auto pilot will make evacuating easier, faster and safer. We always left a "fire bag" in our garage that had our insurance files, personal and business papers and records, and a few other things in it—not as much as we should have had, but at least it was something.

We had a close friend and neighbor who had promised to come by and get our fire bag if there was a fire while we were gone. That's why it was sitting there the night of the fire, ready for me to pick up and throw in the car. Later I realized the folly of expecting a neighbor to have time to come get your stuff, when they most likely will not have time to get their own.

If you vacation during fire season, you could temporarily relocate your irreplaceable treasures off-site, to a friend or relative's home for safekeeping.

Pets, Horses and Other Animals

If you have to evacuate and can't keep your pets with you, the Humane Society or other shelters will most likely be taking small animals like cats, dogs and birds. Keep inoculations up to date, and make sure your pets have collars and tags, RFID chips or other I.D. that lists your cell phone as well as your home phone.

One of my friends was almost trapped in the fire because she couldn't bear to leave her horses behind. In the end, with firebrands raining down all around her, her brother made her get in the car. They drove off sobbing through a storm of embers and flying debris with the unearthly screams of their horses echoing in their ears. They felt like murderers. But when they were allowed back in, all five horses were standing in the middle of their scorched pasture, a bit singed and extremely grumpy, but alive and more or less well. While livestock and large animals can perish in fires, they can also save themselves, and are hard-wired to try. No matter what the outcome, and no matter how much you love your animals, they're not worth dying for.

Find out where you can take your animals in advance, and add the info and the phone number to your emergency contact sheet. Keep an accessible supply of food and water handy. Often the county fairgrounds will be set up to take horses, cattle, goats and other animals too large for the Humane Society or local animal shelter to care for.

Don't plan on being able to make several trips to evacuate livestock. Once you've left, you will most likely not be allowed back in if formal evacuation orders have been issued. If you don't have a big enough trailer to evacuate all your animals at once and a fire is threatening, experts recommend that you open all your gates and let them go. Many horses and other live-

stock have survived after being turned loose. If a fire has been threatening for days, you may want to move your animals to a secure location before you have to. Just remember, if evacuation orders are put in place while you are gone, you may not be allowed back in to get anything. So put your own emergency supplies in the car before you start hauling animals.

CHAPTER 7

Ready & Alert During Wildfire Season

There are many good books and a wealth of other resources that go into great depth on just what is involved in fighting wildfires. You'll find some of them listed in the appendix. The more you know, the more you'll appreciate that sometimes there's nothing that can turn back a roaring wall of flames shooting hundreds of feet into the air, moving faster than you can run, burning at temperatures that can easily melt your refrigerator into a puddle of aluminum and reduce your house to a pile of ashes in a few short hours.

The most important thing for homeowners to understand is that fighting a wildfire is nothing like fighting a typical urban or suburban house fire. House fires usually happen one at a time; fire departments have the resources and personnel to send however many people and engines are needed. They travel on well-maintained roads to reach the fire and usually arrive in minutes. Fire hydrants provide an endless supply of water. And despite all that, thousands of homes in the U.S. burn to the ground and people die in house fires each year.

Protecting people's lives and property has become the number one priority in wildland firefighting. But many wildfires in the WUI threaten dozens or hundreds or even thousands of homes. It's virtually impossible for the coalition of forces that tackle wildfires to defend every home. There aren't enough people, equipment or resources. And when flame-fronts turn back firefighters and raging winds ground air support, all the resources in the world don't matter.

Many people in the WUI live down narrow, winding, bumpy roads with little or no shoulder and few places to turn around or pass another vehicle. Houses are often sited and landscaped to deliberately make them hard to see, which also makes them hard to find. There are seldom any fire hydrants.

And nearby sources of water can be scarce or nonexistent. When you call 911, the fire engines are not going to magically appear in your driveway five minutes later.

The firefighters trying to get up our narrow mountain road were turned back by the same rolling wall of flames that drove us out. We passed the first response team down by our association gate preparing to go in just as we were leaving. We warned them not to go up, and reassured them everyone had been notified and all the residents were either out or getting out. But they tried anyway, only to be turned around, chased back to the county road by smoke and flames and intense heat. Thankfully no one died.

If you live in the WUI you must be prepared for the fact that no one may be able to come save you. You need to be ready to save yourself and your family. Often the best way to do that is to focus on safely escaping before there is any chance you will be trapped in your home or car. No one has ever died in a wildfire because they left too soon.

There are several steps you can take to make sure you are as prepared as possible if a wildfire threatens.

Fire Drill. Have a family fire drill before wildfire season starts. Go over what to do, how to dress and everyone's responsibilities. Make sure your inventory and files are up to date and accessible, and your Important Stuff and Emergency Kit are ready to go (see previous chapter). Review all escape routes, safe places to shelter and basic safety information, as well as your contact person and meeting place.

Daily Maintenance. Make it part of your daily routine to walk your defensible space and clean up and clear downed branches or brush that makes it less defensible. Inspect your roof and gutters, and clear any debris immediately. Make sure you haven't left anything flammable near your house or under your deck.

Monitor the Weather. If a local TV channels offers a custom weather forecast that uses your GPS coordinates, sign up for it. Some networks will deliver severe weather alerts to your phone or email in-box. If not, try *www.weather.com*, *www.weatherbug.com* or *www.wunderground.com.* Pay special attention to approaching fronts and storm systems, and high-based thunderstorms with lots of lightning. Knowing wind speed and direction can help you know which way any fire that starts may move, and how fast.

Keep Vehicles Ready. Don't let your gas tank get down to nearly empty. Keep gas tanks and windshield wiper reservoirs full, and be sure spare tires are inflated. See if there's anything in your emergency kit that can be boxed up and left in your car.

Be Prepared for a Power Outage. Electricity is often deliberately shut off to areas when wildfire threatens. Keep flashlights with fresh batteries on every floor and in the garage. Know how to manually open your garage doors. Keep cell phones charged.

Register All Phones. The phone can't ring if they don't have your number. All of your phones, including all cell phones (even the kids') and Internet (VOIP) numbers, need to be registered with your county's emergency management system for Reverse 911 calls. Each county has their own system so call your Emergency Services department to find out how to register. Taking a few minutes to register your phones now could save your lives. *But if you feel threatened, don't wait to be called; leave immediately.*

....

Know Your Neighbors and Your Volunteer Fire Department

Most communities in the WUI are served by volunteer fire departments that are usually under-funded and short-handed. Getting involved will help you and your neighbors. You don't have to become a firefighter; there are many other ways to help. Creating a stronger community with better resources improves everyone's odds. Your neighbors are often your best lookouts and sources of information, especially if they have wide-ranging views. After a close call with a wildfire in 2000, our community set up a phone and email tree that spread for miles. Some neighborhoods have set up emergency alert systems, using "church bells" or other distinctive noisemakers like air horns or sirens to alert neighbors to an immediate emergency. One of our phone calls the night of the fire woke up a family of five; they credit that phone call with saving their lives.

....

Where Will You Go?

Evacuation centers are quickly set up for most wildfires. They're typically at a local school, community center or fairground and are open 24/7. But now is the time to research your options so you have a place to go if you're evacuated. Even if you plan to stay with friends or family, it's a good idea to check out the hotels in the area. Find out now which ones are pet-friendly and add that info to your contact sheet. If you are evacuated, make the reservation as soon as you are out of danger. Hotels and other housing will book up fast if there is a large fire with a lot of people being evacuated.

If your home is lost, or you are displaced for several weeks or months, as long as your insurance policy includes additional living expenses, your out-of-pocket costs for both temporary and longer-term housing and other expenses will be covered. Chapter 5 discusses this is more detail.

When to Leave

If a fire is threatening, it's better to leave before you have to than wait until the last minute. The longer you wait, the better the chances you could be trapped. And the longer you wait, the more crowded the roads will be. Cars clogging the roads can seriously slow down emergency vehicles and fire-fighters trying to get in to fight the fire. And trying to get out in the middle of a fire that's blowing up is a heart-stopping experience. Many of the 35,000 people fleeing the Waldo Canyon Fire near Colorado Springs described the scene as terrifying, with flames bearing down on them and ashes and burning embers raining down as the bumper-to-bumper traffic tried vainly to move. For many it took several hours to complete a white-knuckle drive that normally takes seven minutes.

People have died in their homes from smoke inhalation and heart attacks, as well as by being trapped as their home was overrun by the fire. Don't risk your life or the lives of your family. Leave as quickly as you can.

Don't Rely on a Reverse 911 Call. Waiting for a formal evacuation notice can be a fatal mistake. Our reverse 911 call came after our house was already on fire, as we discovered when we listened to our voicemail the next morning. And my research revealed many examples of reverse 911 calls that never came at all.

Evacuation orders don't come from an all-seeing computer eye in the sky; they're issued based on information from responders on the scene, working with maps and the experts' best estimates of where the fire is heading. But in a big, active, fast-moving fire, several fire fronts can develop at the same time, resources can be stretched to the limit and keeping up can be overwhelming.

No system is perfect and large-scale wildfires are notoriously unpredictable. There are cases when people called 911 repeatedly and were told they were not in danger, even though they were watching the fire close in on them. The amazing people who work emergency dispatch are trained to be calm and collected no matter how much pressure they are under. But they're not on the ground, and they're not seeing what you or your neighbors can see firsthand. **If you feel threatened, you should leave immediately.**

....

Tracking an Active Fire

Our scanner may have helped save our lives; we knew exactly when the little spot fire three miles and several ridges away that was "almost out" blew up and took off because we heard one of our volunteer firefighters say, "It's gone." And we knew what that meant. A scanner will let you monitor emergency frequencies like FireNet and hear for yourself what's going on and where. Emergency scanners come in a wide variety of makes and models, and start at less than $100 for both hard-wired and handheld. There are emergency services monitoring apps available for smart phones and tablets.

If you have a phone line, be sure you have at least one old-fashioned, hard-wired phone with a cord that plugs into a phone jack. In many cases land lines will still work even if your power is out. Keep cell phones and tablets charged, and leave a car charger for your cell phone in each vehicle.

You may also be able to monitor local emergency responders online; check with your county to see if they have this feature enabled. InciWeb (*www.inciweb.org*) is the national Incident Information System website that provides detailed ongoing updates about wildfires all over the U.S. Every wildfire gets a name; you'll be able to search by state and find accurate information on the size of the fire, percentage of containment, number of firefighters and other equipment on scene, weather, evacuations, structures lost, and maps of the fire's perimeter. It's an eye-opener to visit this website; click on your state and see how many fires are being managed at any one time.

Firespeak: What Are They Talking About?

When you're monitoring an active fire, terms are flying through the air faster than firebrands. When you don't know what they mean, it can be downright confusing, or even scary. Here's a quick look at some of the more common fire terms, and what they mean.

Incident Management Teams. Type 1 and Type 2 Incident Management

Teams (IMTs) are large federal teams that can be mobilized quickly to take over the management of complex fires from state or local teams. There are currently 16 Type 1 IMTs and 35 Type 2 IMTS. It costs over $2 million to mobilize the 60-plus highly experienced people from all over the country who make up a Type 1 Team.

Incident Commander is where the buck stops on a fire being managed by an IMT. The Incident Commander develops strategies, deploys resources and generally holds daily briefings on the progress being made.

Hot Shot Crews are Type 1 crews with 20 to 22 members who train, work and are deployed together. They're stationed in various key areas, but are sent wherever they're needed to work on major fires. These men and women are highly trained, with the fitness levels and experience to tackle the most challenging fires. Right now there are more than 70 of these elite crews.

Containment or Control Line. One of the tactics employed to get the fire under control and eventually out is to put a containment line all around it. The goal: keep the fire from growing any bigger. Lines are created by removing anything that can burn (often by hand) and can incorporate roads, rivers and other natural barriers that can stop the fire from growing.

Contained. A wildfire is considered contained when there is a containment line all the way around it. This isn't the same as being controlled; fires can still be burning actively within the perimeter. Daily reports will usually list a percentage for containment, as in "the fire is now 60% contained." That means there is line around 60% of the fire's perimeter, with another 40% to go. Fires can sometimes jump containment lines. Depending on the size of the fire and fire behavior, people who have been evacuated may be allowed to return to their homes even though the fire is not 100% contained.

Controlled. A fire is not considered controlled until it is for all intents and purposes out, and can be monitored by what are known as mop-up crews that patrol the area looking for and putting out hot spots.

....

CHAPTER 8

Stay Alive When Wildfire Threatens

Don't Gamble with Your Life

In every fire there are people who refuse to go when they're evacuated. The reasons people stay put are complex; the result of refusing to leave or waiting too long to evacuate can be deadly. Some people are lucky, and weather the fire. Some are not. All of them put firefighters and emergency personnel in danger; their number one mission is human safety. Don't make responders risk their lives trying to save yours.

Even if you believe the fire will never reach you and leaving is a waste of time, consider this: even the most highly-trained fire experts don't know for sure how the fire is going to evolve or where it's going to go next. The weather can literally change in seconds; winds can shift direction, fronts can arrive and a mild-mannered, predictable little fire can turn, in the blink of an eye, into a roaring, fire-breathing beast moving faster than a freight train.

A roaring inferno sealed off the only access road just a few hours after the first smoke report.

Time to Evacuate

This one is for real. You've prepared. Now make it pay off.

- Gather everyone together and take several deep breaths. Say a prayer if you are so inclined. Try to be calm; hysteria is contagious *and* crippling.
- Make sure everyone is dressed in long pants (not synthetics; polyester melts to the skin) and long-sleeved shirts buttoned at the cuff and collar. Heavy fabrics like sturdy denim offer more protection; wool is even better. Ditch those flip flops and wear shoes or boots.
- Grab hats, bandanas and gloves.
- Get out your plan. Give everyone a list of responsibilities and a deadline.
- Use your lists to make sure you are taking everything you need.
- Point your vehicles forward so you won't have to backup and do any maneuvering if you have to leave suddenly.
- Know how to open your garage door manually in case you lose power.
- If you'll be pulling a stock trailer, get it hitched up and into position.
- Get your animals ready to load.
- Load your Important Stuff and Emergency Kit into your vehicles.
- Roll up your vehicles' windows and double-check that windshield wiper fluid reservoirs are full and there's a roll of paper towels and a spray bottle of water in each car, or a carton of Wet Wipes so you can wipe smoke off the inside of the windshield.

If you have time: Inside

- Close all your windows and doors, but don't lock them. It delays firefighters trying to get into your home to protect it.
- Close heavy curtains, shutters or metal window blinds.
- Turn off air conditioners and all fans.
- Leave lights on in all the rooms with exterior windows and turn on your exterior lights to help firefighters find your home. Smoke and ash from a fire can turn day into night.

If you have time: Outside

- Get everything that could burn off your deck and away from your home's foundation.
- Cluster lawn and deck furniture downwind and away from the house so it won't snag firefighters' hoses.

- Follow emergency orders regarding sprinklers and hoses. You may be asked to turn them on, or to keep them off. See Trapped at Home (keep reading) for more information.
- If you have any additional water sources, mark them clearly and post a big sign telling firefighters where they are (cistern, pond, etc.).
- Shut off your gas lines.
- Seal exterior vents.
- Remove debris from roof and gutters.
- Leave a metal ladder next to your home, but out of the way of firefighters and their equipment.
- Open gates for any horses or other animals you cannot evacuate. Open coops and barns if you have animals inside.

If you feel threatened, don't wait for evacuation orders. Leave.

Try this trick to calm yourself: Clear your mind and breathe in slowly while you count to four. Hold for four. Breathe out while you count to four. Do this three or four times, and you will be more calm and focused. Clear-headed thinking is vital right now.

Make sure everyone and all your pets are accounted for. Double check and make sure your Important Stuff and your Emergency Kit are loaded in the car. Keep cell phones and supplies handy in case you are trapped in your car. Try not to dwell on what will happen to your house; focus on getting everyone out safely.

Driving Through Fire

We have many friends who had to drive out through smoke and flames. In hindsight, some of them say they waited too long to evacuate. But others left as soon as they could and still were almost trapped. Some of them had to drive over trees that had fallen into the road (thank goodness for massive 4WD trucks). Some people had windshield wipers melt to their windshields.

Wildfires can move at incredible speeds and change directions. No matter how well prepared you are, you could find yourself having to drive through hazards to get out. This is one reason you need to be familiar with your escape routes. If you can barely see or breathe, you need to be able to function on autopilot.

- Drive slowly with windows and air vents closed and headlights on. Watch for other vehicles, pedestrians and animals. Keep moving.
- If you are driving out more than one vehicle, turn on your walkie-talkies. Stay as close together as possible. Dense smoke can turn day into night and make it very hard to see.
- Put your best driver and most dependable, rugged vehicle in the lead. If you're following and get stuck, lay on the horn to alert the lead driver immediately.
- Don't text or talk on the phone while driving.
- Be on the lookout for fire trucks and emergency vehicles; they are often moving quickly.
- If you have to stop, don't block the road.

FEMA advises that if you encounter an obstacle you cannot get around, try to get off the road and park in a safe place with little or no vegetation; don't park under trees. If you cannot get off the road, turn on your headlights and emergency flashers to make your vehicle more visible. Close all windows and doors, shut off all air vents, and turn off the air conditioner. Your car is a dangerous place to try and ride out a wildfire, but in an emergency, staying in your car is better than trying to run on foot unless you are very familiar with the area, the fire has not yet overtaken you and there is a building or a safe place to shelter very close by. If you have cell phone reception call 911.

If you stay with your vehicle, be prepared for conditions that will make you want to open the door and run. Air currents can rock the car. Some smoke and sparks may find their way inside. The temperature inside your

"I wish we'd left sooner. It was like driving through hell." – Survivor of the High Park Fire

vehicle is going to increase. Lie on the floor and cover up with a wool blanket or coat. Stay below the windows, and keep your face as close to the floor as possible. Don't leave your car if the fire overtakes you; most fire deaths are caused by people inhaling smoke and super-heated air and gases. Wait until the fire front passes and temperature has dropped outside before you get out. Stay low when you exit your car and get into a safe area that has already burned so you can assess the situation.

Trapped at Home

Wildland fires are extremely unpredictable. That's one reason it's crucial to be prepared and to evacuate as soon as possible. But sometimes fires develop and move so fast people can't flee. According to the Idaho Firewise Communities program, you can increase your chances of surviving by keeping your wits about you and taking steps to improve your odds.

The first step is choosing the place to shelter with the best chance of withstanding the flaming fire front long enough for the fire to move past you. If you've followed the Firewise landscaping, building and maintenance guidelines, cleared your deck and know your roof is clean and free from debris, that place could be your home. But it could also be an outbuilding, shop, or even a vehicle.

If you choose a building, shelter as far away as you can get from the approaching fire front, but avoid the basement. Stay close to an exterior door and keep flashlights handy. Be sure you have gloves—door knobs heat to searing temperatures. Close all your windows, doors and shutters and take down light synthetic curtains that could catch fire from radiant heat. Shut off all attic fans, whole house fans, swamp coolers and interior fans that could draw smoke and ash into the house. Leave your lights on for as long as you have power; if firefighters are in the area, lights can help them find you.

Even among experts, advice on sprinklers and hoses varies, and can be affected by the behavior of the particular fire. There are cases when residents have been asked to turn on sprinklers and hoses and wet down vegetation or parts of their home; in areas where firefighters rely on hydrants or municipal water sources, people may be asked not to turn them on because they affect water pressure available to firefighters. If you're on a well, running your sprinklers for long periods of time can run your well dry and burn out your pump, leaving you without water later when you might really need it. If you have time and extra hoses, bring them inside to protect them from the heat. Fill bathtubs, sinks and as many containers as you can with water...be creative; trash containers can hold a lot of water. Just put them somewhere you can access them; a 55-gallon trash container full of water weighs more than 450 pounds.

Be sure everyone is dressed in heavy pants, long-sleeved shirts and closed toed shoes or boots. Tuck hair under hats with brims. Have gloves, scarves and blankets at hand. Wool or fire-retardant materials are best; heavy natural fabrics will do. Sheltering under wool blankets or coats can dramatically reduce your exposure to heat and smoke. Avoid synthetics (polyster fleece, nylon, etc.); they melt to your skin and can really burn you.

It's vital to keep everyone calm and together, and keep pets confined. Stay away from windows; you can be exposed to deadly radiant heat and windows can shatter and let in fire.

The roar of an approaching wildfire is both deafening and terrifying. **You'll want to leap up and run outside, but if you do, you'll probably die. Experts emphasize that to survive, you have to stay inside until the fire front passes.** Expect the house to get very hot and smoky. But no matter how hot it gets in the house, it's four to five times hotter outside, and the air is filled with smoke and deadly gases. Stay as close to the floor as possible, cover up with blankets or coats and wait for the fire front to pass.

On average, it takes about an hour for a home to burn down. So if your house catches fire, eventually you will need to escape under the most harrowing of circumstances. The trick then is timing; you need to wait long enough for the main fire front to pass so the air outside is breathable, but not long enough to suffocate or have your house collapse on top of you.

One of the safest places to go is where firefighters seek shelter—into the black. An area that's already burned isn't likely to catch on fire again immediately. Crawl out of the house and stay as low to the ground as possible until you can assess condition outside. Remember, cold air sinks, warm air and gases rise. Both inside and outside, stay as close to the floor or ground as possible; even a few inches can make the difference between air that's safe to breathe and air so hot that inhaling it will kill you.

Once it's safe to move about, proceed with caution. Be on the lookout for smoldering stump holes and trees that could topple over on you. If you have cell reception, call 911 and let them know you are safe. Make sure you know which way the fire is going before you drive anywhere. You may be safer staying put if the fire has already moved through.

If your home isn't on fire and the main fire front has passed, inspect your attic, roof, eaves, under the decks and porches, woodpiles and anywhere else fire could be smoldering.

If You're Caught in the Open

Ready, Set, Go! (RSG) is a program launched in 2011 by the International Association of Fire Chiefs to help fire departments teach people who live in high risk wildfire areas and the WUI how to prepare themselves and their property. RSG works collaboratively with Firewise and other agencies like the U.S. Forest Service. There are already over 500 fire department members from 46 states. This advice on what to do if a fire approaches or you are trapped in the open comes from an extensive array of materials developed under the program by the Ventura County, California, Fire Department.

First and foremost, out in the open is not a place you want to be when wildfire threatens. If you see smoke, and can identify a safe escape route, note your position and the position of the smoke; if you have a GPS, mark your coordinates. If you have cell phone reception, report the smoke and then leave the area immediately.

If the fire is near, don't worry about getting back to the trailhead or your car, get to the closest safe area. This could be a paved road, ranger station, lake, parking lot, or campground. Never, ever travel towards a fire, even if your map tells you it's the fastest way out. Try to avoid trails that cut across hillsides mid-slope and areas with lots of vegetation. And be alert; you won't be the only one fleeing the fire; bears, snakes, mountain lions, moose, deer and whatever else lives in the area will also be trying to escape.

If the fire is very close, ditch your stuff and run for safety. If you see firefighters, run towards them. If firefighting aircraft or helicopters are overhead, try to signal with brightly colored clothing or a signal mirror. They can let firefighters know where you are.

If you are trapped, don't attempt to run through flames to escape. Instead, look for a safe place to shelter. This could be a wide, sandy or rocky beach next to a river or stream, or an open field with little or no grass and vegetation. Lakes, rivers, streams and ponds can seem like a natural choice, but unless you have scuba gear your exposed face can be badly burned. If you're paddling or kayaking, you can go out in the river, flip your boat, and get underneath.

The safest refuge is in the black; an area that has already been burned. It will be hot and dirty, but safer than somewhere the fire has not yet reached. The best temporary shelter is wherever there is the least amount of fuel available to burn. Firefighters are taught to identify safety zones; areas where they can survive without a fire shelter. The Incident Response Pocket Guide carried by all wildland firefighters gives recommendations on locating an effective place to shelter. The guide recommends taking advantage of heat barriers such as the lee side of ridges or large rocks and avoiding any locations upslope or downwind from the fire, as well as saddles, chimneys and narrow canyons, all of which act like funnels for fire.

Firefighters figure out how big their safety zone needs to be by calculating what they call the necessary separation distance, which is based on flame height. For example, if flames were 20 feet high, you'd need to be in the middle of a half-acre safety zone, or an area about 150 feet square. Calculations don't take into account wind, slope or terrain, which can all increase the size of the safety zone. So when it comes to safety zones, the bigger the better.

Be mentally and physically prepared to stick it out under very scary conditions. It's going to be hot and smoky, and the noise alone can be deafening. Embers and firebrands will most likely be flying through the air. If you can, protect yourself with a hat, long-sleeved shirt, long pants, goggles or sunglasses, and gloves. Put a dry bandana over your mouth and nose, and lie flat on the ground.

The biggest threat to survival from any fire is super-heated air, not direct flames. Air that seems to have come straight out of a blast furnace can sear your lungs and kill you in seconds. Remember, heat rises; the air is always cooler closer to the ground, or under the ground if you have time to dig yourself a hidey-hole. Don't panic; there's a roaring sound like a freight train from hell, very intense heat and it's hard to breathe. Smoke burns your eyes and makes it hard to see. People who have been trapped in wildfires report an almost irresistible urge to get up and run. That's the worst thing that you can do. Stay down until after the fire passes and the air begins to cool off.

When it's safe to move, tread very carefully, and keep a bandana over your mouth and nose. Wear a hat, and be on the lookout for hot debris, flying embers, burning sap and falling trees and snags. And beware: wildfires often leave their own version of postholes; tree trunks that have burned down below the surface, leaving a deep hole filled with hot embers.

Notify authorities as soon as you can; if you signed a trail register or anyone knows where you were hiking, people may be putting themselves in danger looking for you. And you may have valuable information about the fire.

Once You Are Out of Danger

- **Meet up with family members** at your designated meeting place.
- **Don't call 911 for non-emergency information.** Your county will most likely have a fire info line set up which will be listed in fire briefings or announced at the evacuation center. Local media and TV stations will have links and info on their Web sites.
- **Don't try to get back in until you are told it is safe.** If you sneak back in, you are putting yourself and others in danger, and could be hampering firefighting efforts. And if conditions change, no one will know you are there. Fire behavior changes constantly. It's not uncommon for people to be evacuated two or even three times for the same wildfire.
- **Stop at the evacuation center**, even if you don't need anything and aren't going to stay there. Checking in will let others know you are safe, and could prevent firefighters from putting themselves at risk searching for you. Many organizations and agencies will be at the evacuation center and at the daily resident briefings that take place during a large fire. This will include the Red Cross and representatives from major insurance companies as well as law enforcement, city and county government and community organizations.
- **Networking with other survivors** will also give you a sense of community, and make you feel as if you are not alone. We found it comforting to know there were people and resources available to help us.
- **If you were forced to leave pets or livestock behind,** contact the Humane Society. Their trained teams may be allowed to go in and rescue animals, even though residents aren't allowed back in.
- If you are involved in a widespread disaster that interrupts communications, you can let others know you are safe by **registering on the Red Cross website** *(www.redcross.org).*

CHAPTER 9

During and After Evacuation

The Waiting Game

We evacuated at 11:30 p.m. The next morning a good friend on the volunteer fire department was able to drive up to our home. He emailed pictures, and less than 12 hours after we fled for our lives in the middle of the night we knew that a pile of smoldering rubble was all that remained of our dream home.

But as I worked on this section, what became one of the most destructive wildfires in Colorado history (the High Park Fire) was raging just a few miles away from our new home. We were safe, separated from the fires to the west by several miles of irrigated pasture lands, roads and lakes, but we didn't need to watch the fire on TV; we could stand on our deck and watch massive clouds of smoke billowing up from the foothills. At night the skyline was a sea of glowing reds and oranges. We had good friends staying with us who had been evacuated. We anxiously followed every shift in the wind

for days, dreading a turn for the worse. When we attended briefings, you could see the pain etched on the faces of hundreds of people waiting for news about the fate of their homes.

We discovered that finding out that your home has been destroyed is not as bad as waiting and wondering. Eventually 259 families would get the worst possible news, and for some that news took many, many days to arrive. And hundreds more, including our friends, would find out their homes had survived.

Evacuations can last anywhere from a few hours to two or three weeks, so be sure when you leave, you're prepared to be gone for a while. In some cases you will not be allowed back in even after the fire has passed through because of fallen trees, downed or destroyed power lines or other hazards.

If you are evacuated, once you reach safety, contact your insurance company and give them as much information as you have, even if you don't know the fate of your home. Make sure they know how to reach you, and you know how to reach them. Many homes that survive a wildfire still suffer damage covered by insurance. And your policy may provide for temporary living expenses (two weeks is common) as long as you were officially evacuated, even if your home is not damaged or destroyed. If your home has been destroyed or seriously damaged, your claim will be given priority over those who have suffered lesser losses.

There are few things worse than looking up into the smoke-filled sky and wondering what's really happening. And rumors spread even faster than wildfire. Your city or county will most likely have information on their website that is updated often. You can often register for feeds and alerts that can be sent to your cell phone or computer.

The National Guard often directs large evacuations.

During an active fire, the National Incident Information website *(www.inciweb.org)* has frequently updated details and fire maps. Since this information is posted by a fire communication specialist, it is often more accurate than the local news.

The Moment of Truth

When I stood at the bottom of
our road and looked up at a 200-
foot high wall of flames roaring
across the ridge my head knew
that our house was gone. But
my heart clung to the hope that
somehow, in some mysterious
and miraculous way, the firestorm would miss us.

One of our neighbors
thought their home had miraculously survived because it was
still standing when they were
finally allowed back in to check
on their animals. Thank God
they never had a chance to open

Burned power poles and downed lines will delay
homeowners from returning to their property.

a door. They were still standing
in their pasture when their home literally crumbled to the ground.

People come face to face with their loss in many ways. Some watch
their home burn down on the news or find photos posted on the Internet.
Some hear from friends or neighbors. Others are told in makeshift confer-
ence rooms set up at evacuation centers or see their address on a listing of
the lost. Some cry tears of joy and relief when they see a photo that shows
their home is still standing.

Whatever the news, no matter how bad or good it might be, there can
be no next steps until you know what you're dealing with. There's a picture
of my husband and I standing in our rubble at the end of this book; it seems
as if just about everyone takes a similar sort of photo. It's as if we need to
convince ourselves this is more than just the worst sort of nightmare.

In many ways, it's much like losing a loved one. Your heart is breaking, but your head is thinking about what special songs should be played at
the service and whether there should be flowers or donations to a favorite
charity. So when you head up for your first viewing, bring a camera and a
notepad along with the giant box of Kleenex.

Your first steps down the road to recovery begin with evaluating and documenting your loss. Take lots of photos of everything that's been damaged or destroyed. If your adjustor comes with you, write down everything he/she says; otherwise it will all be a big blur later on when you're trying to remember. Include photos of your land and your views; you'll need them for insurance and for proving your loss of property value to the county.

Sorting, Sifting and Cleaning Up

Even if your home is a total loss, you will feel compelled to sift through the debris to see if anything survived. With a lot of help from our friends, we unearthed several small things, mostly porcelain and china, that survived at least enough to be recognizable. And we salvaged some colored glass that had melted into interesting sculptural shapes. A couple of rivers of melted aluminum are now inset into our new patio, right below the stone garden bench that once sat beside our pond and made it through the fire with only minor smoke damage.

But damaged or destroyed, your home and property are now full of hazards, some of them with the potential to be deadly. So before you start pawing through the ashes, learn how to sift through and clean up safely. Ash from the trees and vegetation that burn in a fire is mostly non-toxic; ash from structures can be mixed with all sorts of things from mercury to asbestos and lead that turn it into a toxic substance.

Dress for a mess in long-sleeved shirts, pants, old boots, a hat and gloves. We had to buy old clothes and shoes at a thrift store; you may be able to find some at a donation center, or borrow some old clothes from friends.

A good dust mask can help. Masks rated N-95 or P-100 are more effective at filtering out harmful particulates than simple surgical masks or something like a bandana.

Keep kids and pets out. Kids and pets will play in anything and it's not safe for them to play in the debris. There will be all sorts of hidden hazards from broken glass and nails to twisted metal and laser-sharp pieces of china that all have great potential for injury. Plus they will end up looking like chimney sweeps and have to be disinfected and hosed down.

Don't use shop vacs or other vacuums to clean up unless they have a HEPA filter. Regular vacuums don't filter out the small particles in ash and can actually disperse them into the air you are breathing. People with respiratory issues of any kind or heart or lung disease should avoid cleaning up and sifting through debris.

Charitable organizations, friends and family may offer to help sift through the ashes. Many hands can make much lighter work, and make an emotionally tough time a little easier to deal with. The bits and pieces that remain are stark reminders of what once was there. But finding just one thing that miraculously survived can make you feel as if all was not lost after all. For us, some of the small things we saved became symbols of our own survival.

Your county will most likely have a list of available landfills and rules and regulations about disposing of debris. Remember that most insurance policies contain provisions for debris removal. So once you've salvaged anything that salvageable, you can get quotes from debris removal companies and let the professionals with heavy equipment deal with the rest.

For some people, letting go is really hard; there might be nothing there but rubble, but it's all that remains of where you lived and what you loved. Having it hauled away to the landfill ends a chapter in your life you thought would go on forever. But for others, it's the day you can finally exhale. It's a chance to put some of the ugliness behind you and turn to the chapter that lies ahead, still waiting to be written.

CHAPTER 10

Recovery: Picking Up Your Pieces

Recovering from any major loss is a process. No matter how much you would like to push the fast-forward button, the road back to a normal life must be traveled one bumpy mile at a time.

When you lose your home, it's about more than filing your claim and collecting your money and dealing with a million other practical things large and small. It's also about coming to terms with what has been lost, forgiving yourself for all those things you didn't do, and learning to trust again that something good lies ahead. It's about healing emotionally as well as financially.

There will be good days and very bad days. Eventually there will be more smiles than tears. Like all grief, you can't will it to be over, you have to go through it. But you will come out the other side feeling stronger and amazed at your own ability to cope and bounce back. Hang on to your faith in yourselves and the future, and your sense of humor. We used to joke

about having to buy old clothes, and not having to worry about cleaning out the closets. I've talked to many people who journaled, sketched and blogged their way through the worst of it.

If your home was one of many lost in your fire, chances are there are many disaster relief agencies, community service organizations and charities that want to help you. A good place to start is at the evacuation or disaster assistance center. Get information on all the types of help that are available and put it into your recovery file, even if you don't think you'll need it.

You may be offered clothing, bedding, gift cards, kitchenware and other supplies. Don't be selfless; take what you need and think you can use while help is available and easy to find. You'll have something that will be fine for now, and you won't feel rushed into buying things that won't end up fitting into your new life. If you take something you don't end up needing, you can pass it along to someone else or re-donate it. We got a cheery brand new floral coverlet and bedding set at a donation center; it brightened the bedroom in our rental home immeasurably and helped make our existence feel more like real life. When we moved into our new home, we passed it along to another survivor who loved flowers and was just getting ready to decorate her new bedroom.

Just remember nothing is in the news forever; what is organized and available and easy to find right now may be a lot of work to track down or not available later. People have big hearts, but every day there are new tragedies clamoring for attention. Take advantage of as many of the resources that are available to you as you can. Someday you will have the opportunity to be on the giving end once again.

Where To Start

One of your first post-fire purchases should be a big fat notebook and some file folders. And some good pens you like to write with, a couple of highlighters, and some post-it notes. And a laptop if you lost your computer.

Even if you have a memory like a steel trap, you'll feel like your trap has been sprung by an 800-pound bear. The only way to remember what you have to do, who you talk to and what they say is to write it all down every day as it happens. Otherwise by the next day you will forget something vitally important and waste valuable time and energy frantically pawing through piles of stuff. (It's hard to figure out where all the piles come from when everything you own is gone, but they reappear again almost immediately, just like some perverse sort of magic.)

If your home has been damaged or destroyed, the process of filing your claim and getting back on your feet is going to generate paperwork by the pound. Despite doing practically everything on the computer and via email, our final paper files and notebooks took up more than half a file drawer. So get organized from the get-go. Pick a system that works for you, and stick with it.

We ended up going with a five-section notebook with divider pockets in each section. It worked for us, but now I think a three-ring binder with dividers, ruled paper and pocket sections would've been even more useful. We also bought colored file folders to help keep correspondence and other info organized so we could find it when we needed it...which seemed to be all the time.

Therapist Neil Rosenthal, who has lost not one, but two homes to wildfire, has become an expert on emotional recovery. He says that survivors have an almost insatiable need to talk about their experiences to anyone who will listen. But it's good to remember that if your friends don't know what to say to you or how to help, it's unreasonable to expect a lot of emotional support from your cable company.

We found that some of the people and businesses we had to notify were incredibly sympathetic and helpful, while others clearly couldn't have cared less. Make a cheat sheet with information about the fire, including its name and incident number if it was assigned one, the date you were evacuated and the date your home burned (which your insurance company will refer to as your date of loss). Once you start making calls, keep track of each person you talk to and what was said.

Call Now	Call Soon
• Insurance Company	• Post Office
• Family Member	• Service Providers: cable or satellite TV, electric, gas, water, Internet
• Mortgage Company	
• Credit Cards	• Garbage, Newspapers, and anyone who regularly services or delivers to your home
• Schools	
• Work	• Anyone who mails bills to your home
• Banks	• Voter Registration
	• Department of Motor Vehicles (car registrations, drivers' licenses)

Insurance Company. You'll be given a claims number, and if your home was a total loss, you will be hearing from an adjustor almost immediately. See chapter 13 for in-depth information on what to do next.

Mortgage Company. There are no national regulations regarding how mortgage companies must deal with you or your insurance company, or handle your obligation to them (which remains in effect, even though your home is gone). Talk to the loss mitigation department, and explain what happened. Put their information into your contact file, and keep good notes. See chapter 14 for more information.

Family and Friends. There's no good way to break news that starts with "Our home burned down last night," and telling the story over and over can quickly go from therapeutic to mind-numbing. You might want to pick one good friend and one trusted family member, give them all the information, and ask them to pass it along to others. You can catch up with people individually later. I found that sending out a daily email update for a while let me stay in touch with family and friends without having to spend hours on the phone or the computer. You'll feel better if you can focus on moving forward and not spend your time churning. Sending out that email also made me feel as if we were making progress.

Credit Cards. Call your credit card providers and let them know what happened. If they had your home phone on record, give them your cell phone, and make sure they have your email. As soon as you have a new mailing address, let them know; if your billing address and phone number don't match what your card company has on record, you may find your account frozen or credit denied when you need it the most. You'll also be buying a lot of things your credit card company thinks you already own that may trigger a fraud alert on your account. Both of our card issuers temporarily froze our accounts because they suspected fraudulent activity. We appreciated their vigilance and super-smart tracking systems, but since we couldn't charge anything until we got it straightened out, it added stress at a time when we really didn't need any more. You may also be able to get your credit limit increased. Charging things is a good way to keep track of what you are buying, and you might as well take advantage of those rewards programs.

Banks. Notify your bank(s); if you were receiving statements through the mail, this could be a good time to switch to online banking.

Post Office. The Post Office will hold your mail for up to 30 days, and allow you to come in and pick it up. You can fill out a hold request online at *www.usps.com*. After 30 days you can have your mail forwarded to a physical address for up to six months, or you can get a P.O. Box. If you know you'll need a box, get one right away. Smaller post offices may run out of boxes during a big disaster that displaces a lot of people.

Doctor/Pharmacist/Health Insurance. If you lost necessary medications or supplies that need to be replaced immediately, contact your pharmacy and see if you can get replacements right away. Remember to claim any lost medications or supplies that you paid for when you do your contents inventory.

Service Providers. Utilities, cable or satellite TV, the phone company, and your Internet provider all need to be notified so they'll stop charging you monthly fees. Be sure to stop any automatic billing that posts to your credit card or gets deducted from your bank account for services you won't need for a while. If you explain your circumstances, you may be able to get them to return security deposits for equipment that has been destroyed, or waive charges for canceling a contract.

Our satellite TV provider was particularly difficult to deal with, and could not understand why we could not send back our receiver. They insisted on delivering a box to the old address so we could return the receiver; they subsequently charged us a substantial fee when we did not. We resisted the urge to send them back a box of ashes, and eventually located a disaster specialist who apologized and gave us a special package deal when we were ready to reconnect that included a credit for all the charges.

Are there other people who service you regularly who might not know you were affected by the fire and just show up? Avoid charges by contacting them. Some of them may promise you special deals when you are ready to reconnect; make note of them now so you'll be able to take advantage of any offers later when you're ready. Be sure to write down who you talked to and when. It may seem inconsequential now, but it will all add up later.

Communication. The ability to communicate will be your lifeline. A cell phone is good, a smartphone is better and a laptop or tablet will come in very handy. A printer will be a necessity. Assuming your cell phones will to be your only means of communication for the foreseeable future, call your carrier and check your plan; a plan that provides unlimited, or at least more, minutes will save you big bucks.

We kept our landline and voicemail but reduced our service to basic; I later learned I could've put our phone on vacation status; talk to your carrier and explain your situation, and see what your options are. Keeping our phone line let us leave a message on our "home" voicemail advising people to call our cell phones. Ultimately we were able to keep our old phone number when we moved into our new home. My husband left a message on our voicemail that said, "Our house burned down. Call our cell phone at…" I often wonder how many people did a double-take when they heard that message.

The local propane company came and picked up our propane tank for free, credited us with the unused fuel, and released us from our annual contract. We were amazed our tank made it through the fire without either exploding or blowing off the propane, but I've since learned a properly maintained tank that meets  NFPA Standard 58 has a good chance of surviving.

County Assessor. The tax man never rests. Call the assessor's office and report that your home burned down, and ask to have your property reevaluated.

Taking Care of Yourself

The Red Cross says that disasters stir up many emotions: fear for your safety or the safety of people you care about, shock, disbelief, grief, anger and guilt, and worries about the future. Memory problems, anxiety, depression and flashbacks are common. Many people can't focus, and have trouble thinking clearly. Most people can't sleep, and when they do, they have nightmares. It was many weeks before either my husband or I slept through the night, or even closed our eyes without seeing our home on fire.

Children suffer in ways that adults do not; the foundation of their life and their view of their home as a safe place has been shaken. They worry that it will happen again, and that they or their family, pets or friends will be hurt or killed. The unimaginable, unexpected and uncontrollable are difficult for young children to grasp.

Your local Red Cross has a variety of materials specifically designed to help children cope with disaster; they should be available from the teams that will be sent to assist. Helping your kids will help you, too.

Teenagers seem to recover more quickly and function better when they have something to do that helps the family. Giving them jobs also keeps them from withdrawing and shutting down. You can put their Web surfing skills to work by having them help value your stuff. It could be an eye-opener to them to discover just how much it costs to replace all those games and gadgets they loved.

Whether you know your home is gone or are anxiously awaiting news, the world is going to seem like a strange and unfamiliar place. Here are some tips from experts in disaster recovery on how to help yourself and your family:

Return to as many of your personal and family routines as you can. If Friday night is pizza night, go out for pizza. Read a book or tell a familiar story at bedtime.

Rest and get as much sleep as you can. Sleep deprivation really interferes with your ability to function. Yoga, meditation and deep breathing may help you relax enough to get some shut-eye. Avoid working on your claim or watching the news right before you turn in.

Drink plenty of water, even if you don't feel like it. You need to stay hydrated. Being dehydrated can make all the symptoms you're already experiencing worse. Too much alcohol will act as a depressant and interfere with your sleep.

Eat well and get some exercise every day; it will make you feel better and make your brain work better. Happily, dark chocolate is a mood elevator and full of antioxidants.

Don't become a media addict. In a big disaster, TV, radio, newspapers, the Internet and social media will have an almost unlimited amount of coverage 24/7. You will feel compelled to follow some of it, but try to limit yourself to daily official briefings. Getting caught up in the media frenzy sucks up amazing amounts of time, and often just makes things worse. And unfortunately all the news you get will not necessarily be accurate. The rumor mill will be working overtime, and you can totally stress yourself out being distraught over things that turn out to be untrue.

It's okay not to be okay. Recognizing and accepting your own feelings is important. You don't have to keep a stiff upper lip and act like you are fine when you're not. No one is fine after their home burns to the ground.

Do something you love, whether that means going to a movie, having a picnic, or taking a walk. It's important to feed your soul; you are sending yourself a message that life will go on, and can still be good.

Stay connected. Avoid the media, but stay connected to family, friends, neighbors, church groups, fellow survivors and any other support networks that can help. Having people there for you is one of the most powerful things you can do to help yourself get through this.

Don't be too proud to accept help. Many people and organizations are going to want to help you. Accept whatever help you can that meets your needs. It will not only help you, but make those trying to do something feel much better too.

Arrange for counseling if you or someone in your family needs it. The Red Cross can arrange for you to talk with professionals who specialize in disaster stress. Your town, county or church may offer similar services. This may be particularly important for families with children, the elderly and the disabled; the loss can seem even more insurmountable to them. And it's hard for parents to support their kids when they themselves are in need of support.

Take it one day at a time. Recovery is a process. There will be times you'll feel as if you are going backwards instead of forwards. Trust in yourself and the process, and know that over time it will get better.

Helping Pets

If you have to temporarily take your pets to an evacuation center, you can often leave their favorite toys, blankets or a piece of your clothing to comfort them. You will be able to come back and visit them often. The volunteers staffing these shelters love animals and will do everything they can to take good care of them. If you prefer to take them to a boarding facility and if your insurance provides for additional living expenses, the cost of boarding your pets should be covered.

Dogs are soot magnets and will be for months to come.

Handle pets carefully and calmly, especially if you've been separated and are reunited at a shelter or elsewhere they are not familiar with. Pets can become very stressed and react with unexpected behavior; spraying urine, defecating on floors or elsewhere, scratching and biting people or furnishings. That's their way of letting you know they are scared and upset, just like you.

Don't bring pets with you back into the fire area to survey your home or start cleaning up; areas that have been burned and buildings that have been damaged or destroyed are dangerous. You'll be even unhappier than you are already if something happens to one of your pets.

The Perpetual Shopping List

In the beginning you will reach for things many times a day that are no longer there. Some of them will be simple things like a sewing needle and thread, or a safety pin or paper clip. Some will be things you took for granted like your favorite old sweater or cuddly robe. Some will be things that will break your heart when you realize they really are gone forever.

Most of the advice that's out there on rebuilding your life tells you to start with the practical necessities. And goodness knows everyone needs a toothbrush and shampoo and pajamas and deodorant. But one of the first things I bought was a cheery coffee cup and a gently loved teddy bear at a thrift shop. For a few dollars they still bring me many smiles.

Start a list of what you need; try to organize it by type of store so you can cross off a lot of things in one trip. Know from the start that the list will never be complete; every day you will discover more things you need just to go about the business of daily life, especially if you have jobs, other commitments and kids in school.

Keep all your receipts no matter how insignificant. At this point in your life, practically all of them are either additional living expenses or replacements for things you once owned. Make notes on them before you file them.

CHAPTER 11

Moving Forward: Relocate or Rebuild?

People often assume they must rebuild their home on their existing lot in order to collect their insurance, but usually that's not the only option. Typically you can choose to rebuild on site, build elsewhere in the U.S., buy another home, or simply collect the money you are owed based on your policy limits and established value. Ask your adjustor to fully explain all your options, so you can evaluate each one before you make a decision. Everyone's personal situation is different; there are no right or wrong answers, just the answer that's right for you.

Relocating

With some policies, extended replacement coverage (the extra percentage available on top of your basic dwelling coverage) is only available if you rebuild your home; with other policies you can also collect your extended coverage if you buy another home, but you'll need to account for the value of the land. There's an example of how this works in chapter 5.

If you have a mortgage, you'll need to talk to your mortgage company. They have an interest in your home, and if you do not rebuild, you will most likely need to pay off your loan before the remaining funds from your dwelling coverage can be released to you. A mortgage banker can help you work out the best way to handle everything depending on whether you intend to rebuild or buy a new home.

Rebuilding

Rebuilding your home, or building a new one, is obviously a much longer and more involved process than buying a home. It's a long-term partnership between you, your insurance company, your contractors and often your mortgage company. If you've ever built a home, you understand the process, but now there will be a whole bunch of new layers of review and approval. If you are building on raw land, your insurance will not cover the cost of putting in a new well, septic field, phone lines, power lines or other improvements that weren't covered under your policy.

All the same rules for dealing with contractors and deadlines apply. In cases of widespread disasters or other special circumstances, you can ask your insurance company to extend the timeframe you have to rebuild and to continue covering your additional living expenses.

Few contractors are willing to wait until your home is complete to get paid a portion of their overhead and profit. Payments are generally made in increments as work progresses and is inspected and approved, sometimes by both your insurance company and your lender. Make sure that funds will be periodically released for a portion of overhead and profit as well as costs. Find out who will be handling your review and approval process at your mortgage company, and stay in touch. It will most likely be someone in the loss mitigation department. See chapters 5 and 13 for more details.

In many places in the WUI, building codes now mandate more fire-resistant design and construction. Changes in building codes that add costs to your project because they are upgrades from your original construction should be covered up to the limits of your Ordinance and Law coverage.

What About Your Land?

No matter what you decide to do about your home, for better or for worse, your land still belongs to you. If you're going to rebuild, you'll want to start restoring your landscape at the same time. If you're rebuilding on site it may be cost effective to work with your contractor to remove dead trees and other debris that still remains. In most cases your land will need some TLC before you'll

Erosion barriers and reseeding will help save your land from further damage.

be able to plant anything but weeds. If you have significant slope, or sit at the bottom of someone else's, one of the first things to erect will be erosion barriers. Your county or your state forester may be able to direct you to programs that can help you with reseeding, mulching, and stabilizing your property. Depending on your watershed, there may be state or federal grants that can help. Banding together with neighbors can give you more negotiating clout.

In our case, the county lowered property values for all affected properties, and pledged not to reclassify the property as vacant residential land, which carries a much higher tax rate, for at least three years. Even so, taxes were not initially adjusted evenly across the board; our post-fire taxes were twice as high as our immediate neighbor's. We supplied facts and nearby comps and appealed, and the county adjusted them, and even apologized for the error. So if you're dealing with something that doesn't seem fair, speak up. Every jurisdiction is different; discuss your property's immediate and long-term future with your county assessor's office.

There will always be land sharks swimming through the ashes trying to scoop up property at fire-sale prices. The amount of time it takes property values to return to pre-fire levels varies greatly and is influenced by everything from the general availability of land to the impact the fire had on your property and surroundings. If you're unsure about what to do, talk to an independent appraiser and get an estimate of the current value, and talk to a forester about the estimated recovery time. If you're interested in selling, talk to several real estate agents who specialize in rural property. But unless you need the money now, your interests may be better served by waiting until the ashes settle and revegetation begins.

History suggests that immediately after a fire is the worst time to sell; property values generally plummet by up to 50% or more, and most shoppers are bargain hunters. Values generally gradually recover over time, pushed along by owners who rebuild and eventually improve the area, and Mother Nature's long-term revegetation plan. Estimates of recovery range from four to ten years. When we were shopping for a new home, we looked at a lovely log home on the edge of wildfire that had occurred over a decade ago, which was how long the house had been on the market.

CHAPTER 12

Damaged but Not Destroyed

O ur home was a total loss, as were the other 12 homes destroyed by our wildfire. But many wildfires weave an erratic and unpredictable path of destruction that burns one home to the ground while leaving the house next door only partially damaged or totally untouched.

As I was working on this book, hundreds of my former neighbors were dealing with the massive destruction caused by the High Park Fire, which burned more than 136 square miles north and west of Fort Collins during three weeks in June 2012. A total of 259 homes and 100 other structures were totally destroyed by the fire. But many more homes were structurally damaged, some severely, and others sustained smoke damage, or loss of landscaping, fences and outbuildings like barns and garages.

Watching our friends and former neighbors endure what we went through is very hard. It's made me realize that in some ways it may be easier to deal with total loss than to work through the process of repair and restoration. It's tough for an insurance company to stand in the unidentifiable rubble that was once your home and everything you owned and declare it anything other than a total loss.

But with a partial loss or damage, the question of what is salvageable and repairable and what is not can be up for debate. Insurance companies may want to patch and repair things that homeowners feel are too far gone to save and should therefore be replaced. There can be disagreements about the cost of repair and restoration, and what exactly "like materials and quality" means. The process of negotiation and reconciliation can be extremely stressful.

Insurance Questions

You will need a notebook or three-ring binder for keeping track of your claim. It's very important to document all your conversations with contractors, as well as with the adjustor and your insurance company. You'll also want a way to keep things like paint and carpeting samples, fabric swatches, and other choices organized and accessible.

Structure / Dwelling. You have an obligation to prevent further damage, so if there is a hole in the roof, you need to cover it over. But don't repair anything or throw anything away until your adjustor has inspected everything. Even after inspection, take photos and make notes as you go.

The typical replacement-cost policy covers the cost to repair or replace the damaged portions of your home with similar materials and construction. Until the repair or replacement is complete, insurance will pay the actual cash value for the property at the time of loss; when the repair or replacement is completed, they'll pay the rest, up to the limits of the policy.

Typically you have two years from the date of loss to complete the repair or replacement, and 30 days from completion to submit your receipts. If your repair or replacement is subject to new building codes or other laws and restrictions that have gone into place since the original construction, the increased costs should be covered if you have Ordinance and Law coverage, up to the maximum specified. Depending on your policy, demolition and debris removal may also be covered.

Personal Property. If you lost covered personal property in the fire, it's covered under your contents insurance. You'll still need to do an inventory and list all your losses. It will be very important for you to carefully research

replacement value, and provide as much documentation for what your property was worth as you can, because it's unlikely you will max out your contents coverage if you suffered less than a total loss. And if it's not a total loss, limits for scheduled personal property like jewelry and firearms still apply.

You are going to need to turn in receipts to recover depreciation, so keep good track of them. Don't submit original receipts; copies are fine.

Assuming you don't exceed your policy limits, you'll be paid actual cash value for your property up front, and be able to collect the difference between the depreciated value and the replacement value when you actually replace the item and submit a receipt. For example, say you lost a $200 electric drill that was 5 years old. The useful life of the drill is ten years, so it's depreciated 50%. That means your insurance company will pay you $100 (the depreciated value) for your 5-year-old drill. When you go out and buy a new drill for $200 and submit a receipt, they'll pay you the remaining $100.

Outbuildings, such as sheds, barns, storage buildings and detached garages, are typically covered as a percentage of your dwelling (Coverage A) coverage. Landscaping is also generally covered as a percentage of your dwelling coverage, although most polices also specify a maximum dollar amount per tree as well; $500 per tree is typical.

You will want to review your inventory settlement documents before accepting your final settlement check to see if anything has been depreciated more than you think is fair. Depreciation is very subjective; you may be able to demonstrate that your property was worth more at time of loss than your insurance company has allowed. You may have neglected to indicate that the item was an antique or collectible. In the case of a partial loss, every dollar you can substantiate is a dollar you get to keep.

See chapter 5 for a more detailed explanation of insurance coverage.

Inspecting Your Damage & Cleaning Up

If your home was damaged but not destroyed, be very careful inspecting the premises; fire can damage supports, wiring, plumbing and other things that might not be immediately apparent. It's important to have your home thoroughly checked inside and out for damage.

Take lots of time- and date-stamped pictures. Your adjustor will want to inspect your home and decide what is salvageable and can be repaired, cleaned or restored, and what needs to be replaced. You may also want to engage a licensed contractor or restoration company to do a walk-through with you so you'll be more informed when you sit down with your adjustor. Following are a few of the most common clean-up issues.

Debris. Even if your home was not destroyed, debris removal may still be covered by your insurance. Your county will most likely issue guidelines about where and how to dispose of the wreckage. If you hire a contractor to remove debris, get one who is licensed and familiar with the county's guidelines and will certify that debris has been removed to specifications. Debris removal is generally either a fixed amount or a percentage of your dwelling coverage.

Food. The general guideline is "If in doubt, throw it out." Food can look perfectly fine, but dangerous chemicals and toxic smoke can penetrate permeable packaging like cardboard boxes and bags. Food in cans and jars may look okay, but if it's been exposed to high heat, it may not be edible. Throw out any raw foods stored outside the fridge like potatoes or fruit. Even food in your refrigerator or freezer may be contaminated since seals are not totally airtight. If it looks or smells funny, take photos and toss it.

If you lost power for more than 48 hours, the food in your refrigerator and freezer is most likely inedible. If it's been a week or more, don't even open the door. Once your power comes back on, let everything chill and freeze, then open the door, take photos and throw it out. Your food is covered by the contents portion of your insurance. If your refrigerator is under an extended warranty, you may be covered for up to $500 to $1,000 for spoiled food in case of a power failure.

Some people report being able to save their refrigerators and freezers (not the food) with frequent and diligent applications of a mild bleach and water solution (1 tablespoon per gallon) to all surfaces, especially the seals, gaskets and vents. Other suggestions include placing containers of baking soda, activated charcoal or dry coffee grounds inside. If odors persist and cannot be removed, talk to your adjustor before you dispose of appliances.

Smoke Damage. Smoke and soot can sometimes be cleaned from walls and hard surfaces with a mild soap or detergent and a lot of elbow grease. You can't just paint over smoke-damaged walls; the smoke will eventually seep through. You can sometimes clean the area with TSP (trisodium phosphate) and then use an oil-based stain blocker before you paint. If you hire a contractor, make sure they are going to take all the necessary steps for a long-lasting restoration. Fabrics, carpets, furniture and other soft goods present tougher problems. Your insurance should cover clean up and restoration, repair or replacement as needed. Just remember that your adjustor will need to approve things you feel are not salvageable, so don't throw anything away until it's been reviewed. Smoke odors can take a long time to remove, if they can be removed at all. You may need to replace walls, ceilings, insulation and other permeable surfaces. There are restoration companies that specialize in cleanup after fires and floods; talk to your adjustor about using one to clean your house. Get references before you hire anyone.

Beware of Traveling Scammers

Disasters bring out the best in many people...and the worst in others. There are unscrupulous contractors and other service providers who make a living chasing disasters from state to state and preying on people at a time when they are at their most vulnerable.

Don't hire anyone you haven't worked with before without checking their local references and their standing with the Better Business Bureau. Don't rely on their websites or letters of recommendation; these are easy to fake. Your best sources are referrals from satisfied friends and neighbors. And never pay for the total project up front; pay in increments as work is completed, and remember that your bank and your insurance company may want to inspect the work before releasing funds.

Get at least two estimates for any major repair. You can expect that your insurance company may get their own estimate as well, and these estimates may not agree. In that case you will need to ask your contractor to go through the insurance company's estimate and note the areas that are below estimate, and substantiate why his estimated costs are higher. You will also want to go over the insurance company's specifications and make sure they are for the kind and quality of materials you had.

Don't know anyone and can't figure out where to start? Angie's List *(www.angieslist.com)* is an online national referral service that lists and posts consumer reviews for all sorts of providers, from painters and plumbers to contractors. Angie's List charges a subscription fee to consumers, but contractors and providers cannot pay to be listed.

You can also get a list of contractors from your insurance company, although you are under no obligation to use them. Your insurance company will point out that the recommendations are not endorsements or guarantees, and the decision on who to hire is up to you. Just be sure to check references and make sure their work is up to your standards; you are the one who has to live with the results.

Squabbles over restorations and repairs are common; some homeowners report being pressured to accept things like patching carpeting rather than replacing it all, even though the patch does not match exactly, or painting one wall rather than the entire room, or replacing one light fixture, even though you can't match the two that survived. In cases like this you can generally argue that your policy provides that your home and property be restored to its original condition, and patchwork carpeting and mismatched fixtures won't do that.

If you want to upgrade materials, finishes, or anything else (such as a better grade of carpeting, troweled plaster walls instead of sprayed-on stucco, or triple-paned high-energy windows instead of your old double-paned ones), the upgraded portions of the costs are your responsibility to cover.

However, if you want to trade a crate of Gala apples for three-quarters of crate of Honeycrisps, you may be able to do that. For example, if you had a 4,000 square-foot home with four bedrooms and baths and now would rather have fewer bedrooms and baths but more upgrades, you can probably get the new features you would like, as long as the total cost does not exceed what your policy allows. Just be sure to go over your plans thoroughly with your adjustor.

Your contractors work for you, not the insurance company or the bank. But both your insurance company and your mortgage holder may insist on inspecting the final work before issuing a final check.

Facing the Challenges and Mourning Your Loss

Survivor's guilt is common. People wonder why they were spared when others were not. For some, their home may have survived because it was more fire-resistant or defendable. For others it may have simply been the track of the fire or a turn in the weather. Psychologists recommend you try to avoid drawing comparisons and looking for logical reasons. All loss is important. It's okay to feel bad, to grieve for things you cared about that are gone, to wonder what will happen to your property values, to mourn your landscape, to feel overwhelmed by all the work that lies ahead. And in many ways if your home is damaged but can be rebuilt, you have fewer choices than those whose homes were totally destroyed. You will probably have to restore your home, even if you'd rather take your insurance settlement and move somewhere else.

Living in a fire-ravaged landscape presents many challenges of its own, even if your home was untouched. In areas burned down to bare ground, flooding and erosion often become problems as soon as it rains (which always seems to be right after the fire is controlled). Noxious and invasive weeds are anxious to move in but must be controlled, and native vegetation reseeded. Removing dead trees can be expensive, time consuming and dangerous. Proceed with caution if you choose to remove your own trees, or hire a professional. Burned trees that are still standing can be severely damaged and are prone to keeling over with little notice. It's a strange and forbidding landscape that's unfriendly to pets and small children. Every time it rains, the heavy stink of soot fills the air, and when the wind blows, ash and debris often blow in with it.

And yet for many people, home is where their heart is and their land, no matter how bruised and battered, is still their pride and joy. Many people proudly tell tales of gradual recovery and rebirth; of fields that used to be forests sprouting carpets of wildflowers and seedlings pushing determinedly up through the scorched earth, and how birds and wildlife are much easier to see. The land recovers slowly, but it does recover. It may not be the same, but it can still be beautiful.

And many people who have rebuilt, repaired and restored eventually admit that their newly refurbished home is in some ways better than their home was before the fire. This is your opportunity to fix all those little and not so little things you always wanted to.

Wildflowers quickly reclaimed our burn area after the spring rains.

CHAPTER 13

Filing a Claim: Insider Tips and Tactics

If you have lost property in a wildfire, the first thing you need to do is call your insurance company's claims hotline. You'll get a claim number and an adjustor will be assigned to your case. Most major insurance companies have adjustors who specialize in disasters and they are familiar with everything that's involved. If your home was a total loss or severely damaged, your claim will get priority over those who suffered smaller losses. If total damages from the wildfire exceed certain thresholds—often $25 million or more—major insurance companies send in large loss disaster recovery teams.

Your claim adjustor will become your primary contact; in most major losses you'll be working with your adjustor for many months or longer. He/she should meet with you within a few days to review your policy benefits and lay out what needs to be done to collect under each schedule of your policy. You'll also get a formal letter from your insurance company spelling out your coverage in detail under every schedule in your policy and establishing time lines.

Make a copy of your coverage letter, so you can make notes on it. Read it thoroughly, and start a list of questions for your adjustor. It's important that you take time to understand what is available under each of your schedules, and what you need to do to collect.

Your adjustor knows your insurance company far better than you do. An experienced adjustor can help guide you through the murky swamp of stuff you have to do, shepherd your claim through the approval ladder at the home office and help you understand how to get it right the first time.

Ask your adjustor to explain the actual step-by-step process you'll be going through over the next several months, and to give you a rough timetable of how long each phase should take. You'll have fewer unpleasant surprises along the way and be better prepared to hold up your end of the bargain.

Don't be mad at yourself if you don't instantly get it; insurance policies and communications are complicated and your brain is not firing on all cylinders. Just keep asking your adjustor to translate insurance-speak into English. Focus on one thing at a time, and write down all the answers. They may make more sense later. If not, you can ask more questions.

Many consumer advocates advise that if you no longer have a complete copy of your insurance policy (not just the declarations page), you need to make it your top priority to get one, and read it thoroughly. I am a big believer in being an informed consumer, but insurance policies are long and complex and written by lawyers for lawyers, and even the lawyers and courts disagree about the exact meaning of some of the finer points.

So while I would agree you should have a copy of your policy, I'd recommend you put your energy into thoroughly reading and understanding your declarations page and your coverage letter. If there are provisions you simply don't understand or things you are being told that are not what you were led to believe when you purchased your policy, you can check the policy language and ask your adjustor to explain. If that's not satisfactory, you can take the question up the ladder to a claims supervisor. If you are still not satisfied with the answers, you can turn to your state insurance commission for help. In 2011 Colorado's Insurance Commission recovered more than $50 million for consumers who came to them for help.

There will be times you'll talk to and email your adjustor many times each day as you work through the process of filing your claim. Because total loss and severe damage claims can take months or years to settle fully, it's possible you'll end up working with more than one adjustor. That's why it's vital for you to document all your conversations and confirm everything you're told in writing.

Your adjustor will most likely cut you a check immediately to cover some of your temporary living and out-of-pocket expenses while your claims process begins. This check is just an advance; it's not meant to be a final payment. If they don't offer, ask for it.

As adjustors are allowed into burned-out areas, they will want to go with you to assess damages and take photos to document your loss. We were escorted up to our property with our adjustor a few days after the fire. If you visit your property before your adjustor, it's very important that you don't throw away anything or start any cleanup unless you're told to do so for safety reasons by the county or some other authority. In that case, take photos or video everything before you remove it from the scene (turn on the date/time stamp in your camera). If you take photos with your phone, the date will show once you transfer them to our computer.

The claims settlement process has been described by many as worse than actually losing their home. That may be because even though your home burns down in a few hours, settling the average total-loss claim takes between six months and two years. Working on your claim forces you to relive, day after day, the worst day of your life. It keeps you looking backwards instead of forwards. For some people the pain is so unbearable they will do almost anything to avoid dealing with it, which just makes things worse, and delays your ability to collect the money you need to get back on your feet and move on.

Social research shows that the higher the stakes, the more stressful people find any process, and the less tolerant they are of real or perceived service failures.

It's hard to imagine something other than the death of a spouse or child that would be more stressful than losing your home and everything you own. It feels very much as if someone you love has suddenly died. Your whole world has been turned upside down, and your to-do list just to get back to square one is never-ending.

Going through the process of filing your claim forces you to come to terms with everything you lost, as well as everything you should or could have done but failed to do. You will have to put a value on things like family photos and mementos that will be worth far less on paper than they were worth to you. All while you're living in temporary housing without much of anything that feels like home.

It's an ongoing, time consuming and emotionally draining process that requires you to be calm, business-like and rational at a time when you feel anything but. Little wonder few people are well-suited to the task, or that things often don't go as they think they should.

Your insurance company has a contractual obligation to settle your claim promptly and reimburse you for your covered losses. Give them every opportunity to live up to their obligations. Don't go into your claim expecting the worst, or treating your adjustor like the enemy.

If you're hostile, hysterical, irrational or incredibly disorganized, you will make it harder for them to do their job. Save your tears and pent-up anger, ranting and raving for your friends and family. Your insurance company is in the business of writing policies and settling claims. It's all they do, all day, every day. You need to be in the business of settling yours. It's to your advantage to have the best working relationship possible with your adjustor and anyone else you deal with. Approaching it as a job helped us put some distance between our emotions and our stuff, and look at things more objectively.

Maximizing Your Insurance

Your insurance policy is a contract between you and your insurance company. You and your carrier both have obligations, rights, deadlines and long to-do lists. Make it your mission to understand both your policy and your role in the process.

In order to collect your policy maximum on each applicable schedule of your insurance, you will need to prove that your home, landscaping, outbuildings and personal property were all worth at least as much as you're insured for. The way you do that is by "rebuilding" your home, garage and outbuildings on paper to today's codes and standards, and listing / describing a replacement value for everything you owned, from the spices in your pantry to that unusual lamp you got from Aunt Jenny.

You can expect to hear from your agent after you file a claim, but he or she will probably not have much to do with the actual claims process. However many experts say that your agent can be a good source of inside information on how to support your claim and keep things moving along.

Keep Good Records

The process of filing your claim and getting back on your feet is long and complex. You need to keep track of what's happening in a way that makes it easy for you to find and refer to information. Keep all your receipts for literally everything you buy until you're sure you're not going to need them. If you're doing a room-by-room inventory, establish file folders or large envelopes for each room so it's easier to find and submit receipts if, and when, you need to. You'll also want files for your dwelling and related details, a file for correspondence (there will be a lot of papers coming through), and a separate file for additional living expenses.

We used a small notebook to keep a day-by-day record of who we talked to and what they said. Collecting business cards, phone numbers and email addresses made it a lot easier to go back and look things up when we needed to.

Communicate in Writing

Phone conversations and meetings can be very helpful for detailed back and forth conversations and working things out. But for important discussions it's a good idea to send a follow-up letter or email (legally, email is fine) recapping what you talked about and any next steps and timelines. Putting it in writing gives your adjustor the chance to catch and correct any misunderstandings. Having a paper trail will be a big help if you have to work with more than one adjustor. And if any problems should arise down the road, you won't have to rely on "he said/she said."

Don't Lie, Cheat and Pad

As a general rule of thumb, people forced to account for all their personal possessions that have gone up in smoke are going to forget a lot of things. This gives some people the idea that it's okay to claim items they didn't actually have, or to take liberties with the condition or quality of what they do remember. People tell themselves "I'm not cheating; I'm just making up for what I know I'm forgetting."

Honest mistakes are one thing; no one is going to come after you for thinking you had a dozen wine goblets when you really only had 11 because Uncle Harry broke one last Easter. But claiming you lost your grandmother's three-carat diamond ring that your sister back in Ohio actually inherited is insurance fraud. That's a felony. If your insurance company discovers you are intentionally misrepresenting your property, your entire settlement could be at risk and you could suffer serious legal consequences. If they suspect you are turning padding into an Olympic sport, your claim will be subjected to the kind of intense scrutiny that delays settlements. Working hard at documenting your contents and doing your homework will give you the best chance of collecting everything you have coming.

The Difference between Structure and Personal Property

Our adjustor explained the difference between structure and personal property this way: "If it would fall out when you turned your house upside down, it's personal property. If it wouldn't, it's part of the structure." So your cupboards, built-in appliances and light fixtures are part of the structure and covered under your dwelling amount; your free-standing refrigerator and washer and dryer are personal property. Your built-in refrigerator and stove top are part of the structure. The stuff in your car is personal property; the car itself is covered under your automobile insurance.

Coverage A, which is your Dwelling coverage, has many subsets underneath it, including dwelling extensions (detached garages, storage buildings, barns), demolition and debris removal, coverage for landscaping and trees, and some provisions that will come into play if you buy, rebuild or build elsewhere. (Your attached garage is considered part of your dwelling.)

Most provisions under Coverage A are usually listed as a percentage of your dwelling coverage. So if you have $300,000 in dwelling coverage, you typically would have a total of $30,000 (10%) for your detached garage and other structures, and $15,000 (5%) for your landscaping, trees and shrubs. Even though these are automatic provisions in most standard policies, collecting the full value is based on the actual replacement cost of your detached structures, landscaping, trees, etc.; they are not automatic payouts. Your loss will have to be documented. Policies and coverage varies; details will be listed on your declarations page and coverage letter.

Both your home (structure) and personal property are subject to depreciation. If you have a cash-value policy, you'll be paid for the value of your home at the time of loss. That means some parts of your home will be depreciated based on age and use, or wear and tear. For instance, if you have a ten-year-old roof with a 20-year life expectancy, the roof could be depreciated 50%. The actual cash value of your home at the time it burned down may be nowhere close to the cost to rebuild it in today's dollars.

But if you have a replacement value policy, your adjustor will calculate what it would take in today's dollars to replace your home as it was at the time of loss. If you have extended replacement coverage, that amount will be added to your basic dwelling coverage to help account for increases in costs for construction and materials. So if you had $300,000 on your dwelling and

20% extended replacement cost coverage, the total amount you could collect for your dwelling would be $360,000.

Your insurance company will use the information they have on file *and* the information you provide to come up with their own "Scope of Loss" or estimate to rebuild your home using like materials to the same level of quality.

Our building plans had gone up in flames and we discovered the county did not keep plans on file. Luckily our builder's son still had a paper copy. And we were fortunate to have electronic copies of invoices from contractors who'd done home improvement projects for us over the years. We also used photos to document everything from lighting fixtures to built-in bookshelves—the kind of upgrades that make a big difference in figuring costs.

Ultimately we were able to give our adjustor plenty to work with. His detailed reconstruction of our home ran to 64 pages, and added up to considerably more than even our extended replacement coverage. We were able to collect the maximum provided by our policy and eventually our extended replacement coverage. He later estimated that it took him about 30 hours to do our home reconstruction.

Many of the disputes and problems that can arise during settlement are due to widespread differences between the insurance company's estimate to rebuild your home and your contractors' estimates. If your insurance company comes up with an estimate that you disagree with, you and your contractor can discuss it item by item with the adjustor and demonstrate why your numbers are more accurate and more realistically reflect the quality and construction you had. Big discrepancies can result from simple mistakes like specifying hollow core doors when you had solid wood ones, or carpeting when you had hardwood floors.

Getting Through Your Contents Inventory

It's logical to think that if everything you once owned is gone, you'll automatically be paid the maximum amount your contents coverage allows. It's hard to understand why you have to document every single item in detail to collect your money. And it's even tougher to understand why you're only paid depreciated value up front, even if you have a replacement value policy. If the adjustor takes one look at the remains of your home and the limits of your policy and knows you are undoubtedly going to reach or exceed your policy limits, why can't he or she just write you a check?

The insurance industry says it's because doing so would establish a precedent that a claim can be approved without substantiation, and that would open the door for people who are out to pad, cheat or collect something they are not entitled to. Insurance loss statistics show that fraud is no small problem. About 10% of all insurance claims are fraudulent, and fraud costs the industry (and ultimately the policyholders) about $30 billion annually.

I kept hearing that sometimes the insurance company will let you off the hook and just write a check for the full amount, but I was unable to find any company or any policyholder who could confirm that this has indeed happened. Even in states with valued policy laws, contents are usually treated separately and values still have to be documented.

So just assume that you are going to have to substantiate your claim. It takes time, dedication, hard work and focus to collect what you're due. If you have a demanding full-time job, a family to care for, or other obligations that fill your days and make it very hard for you to devote the time needed, it can be tough to meet your deadlines. If you know you're going to have trouble meeting your deadline, ask your insurance company for an extension in writing.

You can also hire someone to do your inventory for you. Of course they'll still need input from you, but they'll do the research, and create your contents list in a form your insurance company will accept. You can also retain a professional company to do your inventory, and in some cases, provide fair market value for your items. Some high-end insurance companies will pay for professionals to complete your inventory.

Whether you prepare your own inventory or hire someone to do it, for every item you claim you'll need to provide a description, year acquired (or age of item), where/how acquired, and replacement cost (if you have replacement cost coverage) or value when purchased (if the item depreciates) or value at time of loss (if it's something that appreciates).

Our contents inventory ran to 168 pages and included more than 2,400 items. We estimate it took us about 250 hours to complete. We turned it in when we'd gone about 30% over our policy limit, even though we were far from done. That overage accounted for depreciation and allowed us to collect our policy maximum. We were then able to use the money as we saw fit, so for us, the extra work was well worth it.

If your insurance company does not provide inventory forms, or you'd prefer to use your own form or one of the many templates that are available, show your adjustor a sample page and make sure the format is acceptable before investing too much time. After you have a page or two completed, show them to your adjustor and make sure you're including all the information they'll need to process your claim.

Depreciation and What it Means to Your Payout

Replacement cost coverage means that you will be paid for the actual cost to replace your destroyed property in today's dollars. The catch is that when you do your inventory, you'll only be immediately reimbursed for the actual cash value of the item at the time of loss. For many items, this will be a depreciated value based on the life expectancy of the item. Then you have to replace the item (generally within two years from the date of loss) and turn in a receipt to collect the difference, up to what you actually paid for the replacement.

Insurance companies all have tables that show them how much a particular type of item depreciates; they are reluctant to publish these tables, but ask your adjustor for general guidelines. Depreciation is not an exact science. You could've had something that was ten years old, but was seldom used and was as good as new. You should be able to make a case that it hadn't depreciated despite its age. And there are whole classes of items, like art, antiques and many types of jewelry, that typically do not depreciate at all.

The general rule of thumb for most non-perishable items is that if an item is one-year-old or less, you'll be credited with the full value. After that most things depreciate for insurance purposes based on their life expectancy. Electronics, technology and soft goods (clothes, bedding, linens) depreciate faster than hard goods (furniture, appliances) and other things expected to have longer useful lives. Your ten-year-old jeans might have been your favorite pair, but on your inventory they'll be worth nothing unless you have replacement value, and then you won't be paid anything for them until you replace them. Your 30-year-old, five-button, fly-riveted Levis are now collector items, and worth well more than a new pair as long as you list them as "vintage collectible Levis" and give a replacement cost.

For example, our five-year-old Kitchen Aid Blender cost $100 to replace; it had a life expectancy of 10 years, so it was depreciated 50%. We were paid $51.85 when we turned in our inventory (they figure in applicable state tax). If we'd then bought another blender for more than $50 and turned in the receipt, we'd have been paid the actual difference, up to a maximum of $50.

If you have $100,000 in contents coverage, and you turn in a home inventory that adds up to $100,000, you'll probably get a check for around $70,000. To collect the remaining $30,000, you'll need to buy the items that were depreciated and turn in receipts. You'll then be reimbursed for the difference between the depreciated value and the actual replacement cost.

Many people really dislike this whole system. It requires a lot of paperwork and it provides no incentive for being a smart, thrifty shopper. And if you want to upgrade something, you'll only be paid for the replacement cost of the item you lost. So some people feel they need to buy things they really don't want to keep from leaving money on the table.

One way to avoid all that is to wait to turn in your inventory until it adds up to *at least* 30% more than the amount of your contents coverage. Experts say that in most cases going about 30% over your maximum will usually account for typical depreciation. If your contents inventory equals or exceeds your policy limits after your insurance company allows for depreciation, you'll get a check for the maximum you have due.

Maxing out your coverage allows you to collect your money with no strings attached. You'll be free to buy just what you want, when you want it. Many survivors discover that they don't want or need to replace everything they lost. And being able to shop sales, thrift stores and auctions will help you stretch your dollars.

Depreciation is a very subjective thing; there are really no hard and fast guidelines. So if you do your best and still come up short, go over your contents inventory line by line and note items that have been depreciated more than you think is fair and be ready to explain why. Perhaps your ten-year-old blender was still in the box and had never been used, and should therefore be valued as if it were new. Or your solid copper tea kettle was actually appreciating, not depreciating. Look for items that have been depreciated in ways that make no sense to you. It's a tedious job, but every dollar you save is a dollar you get to keep. Many people have used a variety of strategies to successfully argue for less depreciation.

Appreciation

You probably owned more things than you realize that were going up in value instead of down. Everything from vintage china, silverware, glassware and jewelry to antique furniture to your 1950s prom dress and your vintage vinyl record collection costs much more to replace today than it cost originally. Some things that I'd bought for a dollar or two at garage sales proved to cost hundreds of dollars to replace on the open market.

Did you own collectibles, antiques, artwork, collector firearms, hand-crafted or fine-wood furniture or a host of other things that not only hold their value but seem to cost more to buy each year? If you can establish identity and value, you will be able to claim their actual replacement cost.

The more items on your contents inventory that your insurance company won't depreciate, the better your chances of reaching your policy maximum without having to deal with the tedium of submitting receipts for everything you buy, or the annoyance of having to pay full-price retail to collect the rest of the money you're owed.

Didn't Own That Much Stuff?

Some people groan that they will never be able to come close to their contents coverage maximum, much less go over it. If you are just not a stuff person, that might be true. But in general, the things you acquire bit by bit over a lifetime add up to much more than you think if you take the time to do your homework.

On our first trip to Walmart after we moved into our rental house we spent more than $1,200. Who knew it cost that much to stock a medicine cabinet, buy a few basic kitchen appliances and lay in a supply of paper towels, cleaning products, toiletries, laundry stuff, and basic office supplies. I looked at the receipt while I was putting this section together. The most exciting thing on it was a bag of Dove dark chocolate squares. It may take a lot of research and a lot of work to value everything (including those chocolate squares, $2.49), but in the end it will be worth it.

If, after racking your brain and doing diligent research, you find you really didn't own enough stuff to reach your policy limits, then you'll need to go the replace-and-turn-in-receipts route. If that's the case, start by replacing the items you want that were depreciated the most.

Pull Together All References

Before you start keystroking your inventory, take time to think about anything that can help jog your memory or support your claim. The more current photos, documents and receipts you have, the easier you'll make it for your insurance company to approve your inventory. If you have high-value items listed on separate riders, there is no need to inventory them again unless they have appreciated significantly since they were appraised for your rider.

Photos. Gather up any photos you have that show the inside or outside of your home. Ask friends and relatives to email or send you any photos taken in your home or on your property. Even something as ordinary as a family birthday party can show things ranging from your countertops to your china and the vintage cake plate you inherited. If your photos are digital, you'll speed along your approval process if you organize them by room. If they are not, perhaps you can enlist a friend to scan them for you and create a digital file you can send to your adjustor.

Bank and Credit Card Records. Your checking account and credit card records can help remind you of what you owned and document purchases; just remember that if you were a thrifty shopper who bought things on sale, you will need to research replacement cost at full retail so you can claim full replacement value.

Online Order History. Many online retailers can provide you with many years of order history; this can be even more helpful than credit card records, because your order history will include more information about the actual items.

Retailer Records. Department stores, discounters, furniture stores, electronics stores, catalogs and other companies often keep detailed records of shopper purchases; these days everyone is trying to better understand the customer. Contact retailers you do business with and ask them if they are able to provide you with an order history.

How to Research Replacement Value and Price Your Stuff

Assuming you have replacement cost coverage, you'll need to research the cost of buying the items you lost on the open market at full retail price and provide that information to your insurance company. So what are the easiest, most efficient ways to price your stuff?

Wanding Your Way to Value. These days almost all retailers use electronic inventory management. When brides and expectant moms register for gifts at major retailers they're given a wand and allowed to roam the store scanning everything their heart desires. The store then uses the results to create their gift registry. Even retailers without gift registries typically use portable wands to scan items.

If you talk to the store manager and explain your circumstances, they may let you go through the store and scan everything you used to own, or a reasonable facsimile thereof. When you're done the store can print out a list with item descriptions and a retail prices. Since you'll be roaming from department to department, your list will be well organized. This is an easy way to get pricing on hundreds of items without having to go from store to store with a clipboard. I sure wish I'd known about this trick in time to have used it myself.

Walking About. Simply walking through stores is a good way to collect a lot of pricing information and jog your memory; you're sure to see things you used to own that you've forgotten about. Just avoid discount stores; finding bargains works against you. If you list items that are on sale, record the regular retail price. If you're wandering around with a clipboard or notebook you may want to check in with the manager so the store doesn't think you are sleuthing for a competitor. You never know, they may offer to help you.

Internet Sources. The Internet is a tremendous research tool if you know how to use it. We used online resources to value everything from elk antlers and handcrafted log furniture to Victorian wicker, vintage jewelry and hundreds of other items that would have required trips to many specialty stores to price.

Most major retailers have extensive websites these days, but so do millions of specialty retailers; the Internet has made it possible for virtually anyone to compete on the world-wide mall. Learn how to bookmark sites you use so you can easily return to them. You can also copy the Web address out of your browser before you leave the site, and paste it into a document that lets you keep track of all the Internet sources you used. Or add a column to your contents form. It's a little more work up front, but it will make it much easier to substantiate a price if your insurance company has any questions. (If this section seemed like it was written in techno-babble, ask a tech-savvy friend or relative to teach you the basics and help you until you get the hang of it. You'll save a lot of time and aggravation in the long run, and learn skills that will come in handy in the future.)

More Tips for Getting It Done

Take It One Room at a Time. Doing your inventory is like eating an elephant...it's something you have to do one bite at a time or you'll choke. Or throw up. Insurance companies uniformly advise you to do your inventory room by room, because it helps you focus. I'd agree with that, but I'd add a time-saving tip: if you are pretty sure your contents will go at least 30% over your policy maximum, start with the highest-value room, and value the items first that are the most expensive and will be depreciated the least. That way you might be able to avoid inventorying your sock drawer or collection of canned soup. If you are an avid cook, your kitchen might be packed with expensive cookware, knives and gadgets. If you just took delivery of all new furniture for your great room—as we had, one week before the fire—that's a great place to start.

Be Goal Oriented. Don't think about how far you have to go; let yourself celebrate how far you've come. Keep a running dollar tally for each room, so you always know how you are doing. When you get to that halfway point, you can cheer. Reward yourself by doing something fun every time you finish a room.

Visualize. Use your photos for room-by-room reference. Close your eyes and pretend you are walking into a room. What do you see? Write it all down; you can value it later. Open the cupboards; what's in there? (Don't scream!) Do the same for closets and other storage areas. "Look" under your feet, on the walls, up at the ceiling. Think about holidays, special occasions, family trips and outings to conjure up those infrequently used things you've forgotten about.

Category Tips

Antiques and Collectibles of all varieties generally go up in value each year; as dealers always say, "they aren't making any more of these..." So instead of depreciating, most antiques appreciate.

You might think you didn't have any antiques or collectibles, but what about your Grandmother's dishes, the button collection you inherited, that jar of marbles you've had since you were a kid, your collection of Nancy Drew books, those embroidered tablecloths, your Dad's collection of fishing lures or duck decoys or pocket knives, your Mom's cookbooks, your Hallmark Christmas ornaments....the list could go on and on.

Even I was shocked to find out it would cost me over $300 to replace my gallon-sized mason jar full of old glass marbles. One survivor I talked to discovered that the family sterling silver tea set was worth over $10,000. Many things get harder to find, and more expensive, every year...from Bakelite handled ice cream scoops to wooden rulers. If it wasn't new, take the time to look it up before you dismiss it as a bunch of old junk.

You can use an online antique mall like *www.etsy.com* to value antiques, or you can visit a few antique stores to see what things are going for. There are dozens of price guides for antiques, from general guides like Kovel's and Schroeder's to specialty guides for specific collections. Current guides provide what is known as "book value," which is generally considered equivalent to replacement value with no dickering. I would avoid Ebay except for the "buy now" items; in most cases, auction results are not a good indicator of true replacement value.

Handcrafts can be very expensive to replace. You may have bought or inherited handmade furniture or accessories, or made things yourself. When you're listing these things as contents, you need to find out what you'd have to pay someone today to make them for you. The older and more unusual the handcraft, the more expensive it will be to replace. Embroidery, crochet, needlework, quilting, woodworking, pottery, blown and stained glass and hand-tooled leathers are just a few examples.

Photo albums, snapshots and framed photos are among the things that mean the most to many people. You can't charge your insurance company for sentimental value, but you can count the actual cost of taking and developing photos, the cost of replacing frames and the high cost of vintage photography and frames. We worked out a formula with our insurance company that allowed us to use a set cost for each size of print, based on the cost of film today (yep, they still sell film) plus the cost of developing and printing. We divided photos into size groups, and counted them accordingly. If you have 20 albums that each held 600 photos, that can add up pretty quickly. You can also research the cost of frames, mats, storage boxes or anything else. Did you have any old family photo albums? Old tooled leather and celluloid albums are now very collectible, and can go for several hundred dollars each. Were you into scrapbooking? All those albums and supplies really add up.

Artwork. If you had original art but did not have appraisals, you can still establish value by contacting the artist or an art appraiser. Even if your art was nice prints or treasures you scooped up at garage sales, what matters is what it costs to replace. Don't forget the cost of custom framing.

Music. Modern music is fairly easy to value; you can use the price of new CDs for reference. Exceptions might be rare or out of production CDs and signed CDs that would bring more than face value on the collector market. If your iPod melted in the fire with 2,000 songs on it, you need to add up the cost of rebuying all that music unless you had it backed up on a hard drive that survived, or still have the online account to re-download. Surprisingly, those old vinyl albums you've been carting around since college may be worth even more. I discovered that many old albums in every genre are now collector's items, and cost many times more than a new CD with the same music. You can check out prices at *www.vvmo.com* or other websites that specialize in collectible music.

Books. Most hardback books can be valued at replacement cost as long as they are still in print; if they are out of print, they might cost more to replace now than they cost new. Current editions of textbooks and reference books should not be depreciated, even if they are several years old. Old editions of reference books may be devalued unless you can show they have collectible value. Rare and unusual books should be priced individually; visit a rare book store or check out online. Vintage cookbooks, some children's books, and first editions (even of modern authors) are part of the long list of books that appreciate in value.

Settling Your Claim

The process of settling a claim that most likely runs into the hundreds of thousands of dollars is time consuming, complicated, emotionally distressing and often confusing. It's easy to turn the normal bumps in the road into roadblocks, because you just want it all to be over. Or as one survivor put it, "We want to look ahead to the future, and they keep making us focus on the past."

One of the first things our adjustor told us was that his job was to help us collect every cent we were entitled to under our policy. We took him at his word and he more than lived up to it. We collected our policy limits under each applicable policy provision except for our additional living expenses, and that was because we found someplace to call home well before our additional living expenses would have run out.

He gave us all sorts of tips on doing our inventory and didn't try to low ball the cost to rebuild our custom log home. He made sure we knew how to list our antiques, jewelry, rare books and many other items that had appreciated in value instead of depreciated, so we would be able to collect their full replacement value. He explained how to use our extended replacement cost to cover the gap between the policy limits of our dwelling coverage and the cost of the 22-year-old log home we eventually bought, along with upgrades and remodeling that brought it more in line with the home we lost.

He called us evenings and weekends; he called us while he was on vacation and left us with one of his partners to help us. He stuck with us from the day we all went up and walked around in a daze in the still smoldering remains of our home until the day they wrote us the final check.

We had as good an experience as I think it is possible to have when you are going through one of the worst times in your life. In the course of my research I talked to many people covered by many different insurance companies who were as satisfied as I think it is possible to be with their settlement and how their claim was handled. But I also came across people who had suffered similar losses whose claims' settlement process sounded remarkably similar to a two-year-long root canal with no anesthetic.

I was so perplexed at the range of experiences that I talked to our adjustor about it, as well as adjustors from other companies and several industry analysts and other experts. A common thread emerged: settling an insurance claim is a two-way street. Sometimes insurance companies do make mistakes or try to settle claims for less than someone deserves. Some claimants and adjustors just don't get along. And while it's true that some adjustors and some companies are better and easier to deal with than others, some claimants are also easier to deal with and better able to tackle the tremendous task that lies ahead.

If you listen to your adjustor, ask the right questions, follow the policies and procedures and timelines you are given and keep on top of the process, you have a much better chance of winding up in the totally or mostly satisfied column. If you go into your claim expecting the worst and behaving accordingly, your odds of having a good experience go down.

Our adjustor's boss stood amidst the blackened piles of our rubble a few days after the fire and gave us some good advice. He said we needed to think about all the work we would be doing to substantiate our claim as a job, with a really big payday when we were done. It was going to be a lot of hard work, but it would pay off in a maximum settlement.

My husband and I have both been in the marketing and communications business for years; I'm sure that made it easier for us than for many others to put on our work hats and focus on the task at hand. Sometimes it almost felt as if we were working on a big research project for a client instead of dissecting our former life and offering it up to be valued. It hurt, but we were able to push through it.

Start out with a realistic timetable and to-do list. Accept

To Do

* ✱FIND building plans
* • LOOK AT RENTAL HOUSES
* • GET MODEL # FOR TV
* • PRICE CARVED BEAR ON DECK
* • ~~ASK MOM ABOUT CHINA PATTERN~~
* • TIMETABLE W/ADJUSTOR
* • HOW OLD WAS FRIG?
* • ~~ORDER NEW CHECKS~~
* • NEED DRESS FOR WEDDING
* • ~~PRINTER PAPER~~
* • RELIEF CENTR - KITCHEN STUFF
* • BUY MASKS FOR SIFTING ASHES
* • BORROW OLD CLOTHES
* • BUY CALENDAR

the fact that nothing is going to happen overnight. Make sure you understand all the steps involved, and what is expected of you. And what you should expect of your insurance company.

There were times during our settlement process we were convinced that "they" were trying to prevent us from collecting everything we had coming. Instead of calling a lawyer or turning to a public adjustor, we would pick up the phone or send an email, and keep asking questions until we understood what was going on, and what we could do to move things forward. I'm glad we stuck it out. We moved into our new home in less than six months, so I doubt hiring a professional to handle our claim would have sped up the process any. And since we were able to collect our policy limits, a professional's fees would have eaten into our settlement. We could have collected more if our limits had been higher. But the fact that we turned out to be underinsured—as many people do—was our responsibility, not our insurance company's. We'd been intending on increasing our coverage when we got back from our vacation, but we never mentioned it to our agent. That decision was just one more thing we learned to let go and put behind us.

Where's Your Money?

After certifying your loss, your adjustor will most likely be able to advance you a percentage of your various coverages. Make sure there is no language on the checks to the contrary, but a series of partial checks is the norm; they're not intended to be final payments. You'll be paid the remaining amounts you're entitled to collect under each coverage provision as your claim progresses and sections are completed. Remember, if you have a mortgage, your mortgage holder legally has an equal interest in your insurance proceeds. Checks issued under your dwelling and dwelling extension coverage are generally made out to both you and your mortgage holder, and sent to them for safekeeping, typically in an escrow account. You need to talk to your mortgage holder about how funds will be dispersed and how your mortgage payment will be made. If your money is being held in an interest-bearing account, ask how you will be credited with the interest earned.

When Things Go Wrong

If you feel that you are doing your best, meeting deadlines and providing what is asked for and your adjustor or insurance company is not living up to their end of the deal, the first thing to do is to talk to your adjustor, go over the list of things that don't seem to be right to you, and give him or her a chance to explain and resolve any issues.

If you've tried in good faith to work with your adjustor and you don't feel you're getting anywhere or are being treated fairly and professionally, your agent may be able to intercede on your behalf. You can also ask for a claims supervisor, who may be able to work things out or assign you to a different adjustor. If you still can't resolve your issues, you can appeal to your state's insurance commission. The insurance commission has a lot of clout, and it's part of their job to look out for consumers and step in when necessary.

If you've exhausted all your free resources and are still not satisfied, you can consult an attorney who specializes in insurance law. Just be aware that attorney's fees will reduce your final settlement. On the other hand, insurance companies dislike going to court, because court rulings become a matter of public record and can set precedents all across the country.

Should You Hire a Public Adjustor?

I work out of my home and do a lot of research in the course of my job as a writer, and my husband is retired. We don't have any kids to worry about. So we were able to dedicate a lot of time to settling our claim. Some people don't have the time or the skills or just can't face dealing with a complicated process that is going to go on for months. If that describes your situation, there are various professionals who can help you settle your claim.

Professional inventory companies work for a fee, but don't handle negotiating with your insurance company. Many of them do not provide values for your contents, just lists.

Most public adjustors take a percentage of your settlement as their fee. Public adjustors typically charge about 20%; in a major claim that is a lot of money. If a professional can help you collect substantially more than you could collect on your own, or if simply not having to deal with the process is more valuable to you than keeping all your money, it may be worth it.

If you are going to consider hiring a public adjustor to handle your claim, be very careful to thoroughly check references, read the contract, and have it reviewed by a lawyer familiar with insurance claims. Ask how many claims he is currently handling; if a public adjustor bites off more than he can chew, he will delay your settlement process rather than move it along. And remember, you are still going to have to provide a lot of input and information. No one knows your home and your belongings the way you do.

Public adjustors work for you, not the insurance company, and the good ones are well-versed in insurance policy language, provisions and laws. Public adjustors must be licensed in your state, and are not supposed to chase disasters soliciting business. The National Association of Public Insurance Adjustors *(www.napia.com)* offers referrals by state. Experienced public adjustors can earn advanced certification (CCPA) and adjustors with at least ten years of experience can earn the Senior Professional Public Adjustor designation (SPPA).

Only you can decide what it is worth to have someone else take over the job of settling your claim. There's no guarantee a PA will get you any more money, or get it any faster, than you can on your own, but they answer only to you.

Insurance Lawyers

If you feel you have done your best to settle your claim according to the procedures you've been asked to follow, you've worked with your adjustor to the best of your ability, you've talked to upper management at your insurance company, gone to your state insurance commission and you're still not getting anywhere, a good lawyer familiar with insurance law can help you unravel the legal issues and obstacles and develop a list of sound legal-based arguments you can use with your insurer.

It's not necessary to sue anyone to benefit from a lawyer's advice and guidance. Just be aware that if you hire a lawyer on contingency, they will get a percentage of your settlement. If you hire a lawyer by the hour, you can pay for the advice you need. And you can hire a lawyer to negotiate for you without hiring them on a contingency basis. Suing your insurance company is a last resort to be used when all else has failed and you have nothing to lose.

CHAPTER 14

Financial and Tax Considerations

Mortgages, Liens and Notes

Do you have to keep paying your mortgage(s) and taxes even though your home has burned down? You bet. Your mortgage holder(s) have an equal interest in your insurance proceeds, up to the amount you owe.

There are currently no national regulations that dictate how mortgage companies must handle insurance proceeds. Policies and procedures vary by bank or mortgage holder. Issues are usually dealt with by the loss mitigation department.

Industry experts advise that you contact your mortgage holder immediately, explain your situation and start working out a process that will work for you. The higher up the ladder you go, the more leeway the person you're talking to will have. Some lenders will make special arrangements, particularly in a fire with large-scale losses. Some lenders can be very difficult to work with, and it can be tough to get them to release funds to contractors if you are rebuilding. If you are having issues you cannot resolve, you can contact the Federal Reserve for help, as the majority of mortgages are underwritten by the Department of Housing and Urban Development (HUD).

One enterprising homeowner was being told to continue making mortgage payments even though the mortgage company had received more than enough funds from the insurance company to make payments. They finally contacted their U.S. Senator, who interceded on their behalf, and convinced the mortgage company not only to take the payments out of the funds they were already holding, but to credit the homeowner with interest from the day the funds had been received.

Insurance companies have different ways of handling their fiduciary responsibility to satisfy any outstanding debts on your home, including liens. Sometimes all checks for the dwelling amount are made payable to both you and your mortgage holder but sent to the mortgage holder for safe keeping in an escrow account. If the escrow account earns interest, you may be entitled to it, but you will probably have to ask your mortgage holder.

If you once had a mortgage and paid it off, but neglected to notify your insurance company—as we did—you will have to get a release before your insurance company can make out checks solely to you. Luckily we had ours in our important-papers file; if we hadn't, our dwelling settlement would have been delayed.

Sometimes your checks for payments for monies due for things other than your dwelling will end up at your mortgage holder as well; in that case, you need to ask the mortgage company to endorse the check if that's required and send it to you.

If you are not rebuilding, your insurance company may ask for a certified copy of the payoff on your mortgage and issue a check directly to your mortgage holder for the balance before paying you. Your mortgage holder should then release you from your mortgage note.

If you're rebuilding and financing the construction, the process can be even more complicated. Your mortgage holder has an interest in making sure that your home is rebuilt to its previous condition and may want to inspect the work being done before making periodic payments to your contractors. Many people report having problems getting the mortgage company to release funds to contractors, who understandably expect to paid as work progresses. This is a process you need to work out with the loss mitigation department.

Property Taxes

You're going to be irritated when you get a property tax bill for a home that is no longer standing, or is now sitting in a black moonscape with far-ranging views of more of the same. Most counties have a complex property review and evaluation process that results in you paying your taxes "back" instead of forward. So in 2011 when our home burned down we were paying property taxes from 2010, when our home was still standing.

You need to make sure your property is properly revalued going forward and that it is not automatically reclassified as vacant residential land, which could carry a much higher tax rate than residential developed land.

This is important whether you are rebuilding on site, selling your property, or just going to hold on to it for a while.

Your county assessor will probably visit all the properties involved as soon as practical. But don't count on them to automatically slash your values or your taxes. Or to reduce them equally. Be your own advocate. Submit documentation with photos if you have them, state the before and after value, and ask for an adjustment that removes the structure portion of your property, and adjusts the land value based on its condition.

People whose homes were not damaged or destroyed by the fire can also see their property values plummet. Anyone inside or close to the fire's perimeter should consult an appraiser or real estate expert, see how their property value has been impacted and then apply to the county for a reduction in assessed valuation.

Tax Planning and Uninsured Losses

Even people who are insured typically face losses that are not covered or exceed their coverage in a total loss. Those losses can often be used to reduce both your federal and state income taxes, and can often be carried forward or back. The rules are a bit complicated, but the payoff can be substantial. Unless you are a tax whiz, it's a good idea to consult a tax specialist familiar with disaster losses.

If a wildfire has been declared a federal disaster, there are special benefits available to survivors. These benefits vary by disaster and the amount of relief granted and available, but can include financial relief for the underinsured and uninsured, as well as tax benefits and special low or no-interest loans for small businesses. FEMA and the Small Business Administration can provide more information and applications for relief.

CHAPTER 15

Our Story

We were having a farewell dinner of sorts at our home on Friday night, April 1, 2011. We were heading to Florida on Sunday and wanted to spend some time with our good friends LaVonne and Rex Ewing before we left. LaVonne and I noticed the grayish plume lazily snaking up into the sky at about the exact same moment.

"That's not a cloud," I remember saying, as I got up to turn on the scanner. We listened in as firefighters tried to locate the fire, which had apparently just been reported. The location given was about three miles south of us in a remote area with scattered homes and cabins tucked into a dense forest of ponderosa and lodgepole pines, Douglas fir and blue spruce.

We'd all been evacuated before, and over the years we'd monitored too many wildfires to count. We took turns looking through the binoculars and listening to the responders. Eventually we went back to eating dinner, with one eye on the sky.

The next morning the fire had a name. The Crystal Fire was reported at just 25 acres and 90% contained. Dozens of firefighters were on the scene. We couldn't see or smell smoke anymore. We heaved a sigh of relief and returned to packing for our trip.

My husband Cory and I lived on 72 mostly wooded acres a mile and a half up a winding, one-way mountain road. We were constantly thinning and trimming, but the winter had been so dry we hadn't even been able to burn our slash piles. Officially it was still winter, but there had already been a couple of wildfires. Something gnawed at me to take the time to go through our house and take those pictures I'd been meaning to take "just in case."

In less than two hours I'd taken more than 75 digital photos. I even opened up all the drawers on the old map case that served as my jewelry cabinet. I snapped shots of the garage and the shed and, heaven forbid, the insides of my over-stuffed closets. I kept telling myself it was because we were going out of town. Later on people told me I must have had an angel on my shoulder.

I remember getting the duffel bag that we used for our fire bag out of the garage where it spent every fire season and making sure that our important papers and documents were in there—our financial records, birth certificates, marriage certificate, insurance policies, files on the cars and our tax file. (I could hear our accountant yelling: "Save the tax records, Linda!")

Not even a trace of smoke snaked up from the ridge across the valley. But I grew more uneasy as the day went by. Eventually I added a small plastic tackle box with some family jewelry, and Cory's extra prescription medications to our fire bag. I thought about packing more, but our house was filled with things we couldn't really replace; once started, I feared we'd need a moving truck. And after all, the fire was more than three miles away and almost out. I wish I'd taken another hour or two that Saturday and packed a few more memories, instead of convincing myself it would be bad luck to pack too much, as if being prepared was somehow inviting disaster.

Later that afternoon I went out to say goodbye to our beautiful land...I just didn't realize that's what I was doing. We were proud of our tree farm; a national designation that certified that we were following a ten-year plan developed by our state forester to manage our land for forest restoration and health. I walked through our property, admiring the effects of several years of hard work.

I wanted to take my favorite hike one more time before we left, so I tramped down our old association road and into Roosevelt National Forest. Despite the dry conditions the pasque flowers were blooming, the bluebirds had returned and there were other signs that after the long dry winter, spring was almost here. I was looking forward to spring snow storms bringing much-needed moisture, the hummingbirds returning and the grouse drumming their mating song.

As day turned into night the wind picked up. We kept watching the ridgetop and turned the scanner back on, but there was still no smoke to be seen. The fire was reportedly under control, with a skeleton crew on scene to "fire sit" through the night. I remember thinking it was a good thing they'd gotten it out the day before. By the time we finally went to bed, the wind was wailing and howling through the upstairs gutters; that's why I was downstairs in our basement guest room trying to sleep when I heard a huge boom sometime after 11:00. I ran upstairs to look out the deck doors into the night; the entire ridge to the south was glowing an ominous red. I screamed up to Cory; we flipped the scanner back on just in time to recognize the voice of one of our volunteer firefighters saying, "It's gone."

We knew that meant the fire had blown up, but we couldn't tell which way it was going; the fire front could stay on the back side of the ridge and miss us, as the Bobcat fire had done 11 years earlier. But we started packing up for real anyway.

I ran up and down loading duffels packed with shorts and flip-flops into the car while Cory called all of our neighbors. In the time it took to throw two duffel bags, my laptop (no time to load up Cory's desktop) and the fire bag into the car, the wildfire had made up its mind.

When the flames started spilling over the ridge and pouring down into the valley, it looked just like the tsunami in Japan, except it was a wall of flames that was descending on our neighbor's home. We'd already called them; we knew they were trying to round up their horses. Cory made his last phone call and we fled. We still had to drive a mile and a half in the dark down our smoke-choked association road before we'd reach the county road; from there it was 45 minutes to town.

On the way down we almost collided with another neighbor trying to bring in a big horse trailer to help with evacuations. There was no way to pass, and he couldn't back down. For a few tense minutes we thought he'd have to unhook his trailer and push it over the cliff so we could all escape. Finally we were able to inch our car down the side of the mountain far enough for him to squeeze by. We warned him not to go up.

Near the bottom of the last hill we detoured up the driveway of a neighbor who hadn't answered the phone. Cory let himself into the house, banging on doors and yelling at the top of his lungs so he wouldn't get shot.

I remember stopping to look up at the ridge some 700 feet above me and thinking that nothing could possibly survive that; the entire top of the mountain was an inferno. Flames were shooting hundreds of feet into the sky, and blazing wind-driven embers were raining down everywhere. Our house was on the other side of that wall of flames.

We ran into a team of firefighters on their way up as we finally turned onto the county road. We told them that everyone had been called and was either out or coming out, and warned them not to try to go in. They started up anyway. Later we found out that both our neighbor with the horse trailer and the firefighters had been forced to turn back by the flames and smoke and incredible heat before they could get anywhere near our home, or anyone else's.

We parked under the brightest lights we could find at the motel; everything we owned was now in the backseat of our Ford Explorer. We were worried about Rex and LaVonne; they live off-grid and hadn't answered the phone when we'd called to warn them the fire was headed their way. Later they discovered that two other friends had called right at the same time we did, but their Internet-based phone put all three calls into voicemail.

Thankfully LaVonne is as light a sleeper as I am; she'd been woken up by the wind or her sixth sense or perhaps that angel on my shoulder soared over the flames to find them. They now think if they'd woken up when we called, they might've been driving on the ridge road when the super-heated fireball traveled from our hilltop to theirs. As it was, they'd had to drive out through walls of flames and blinding smoke.

They called from their car at 1:39 in the morning. No one could sleep; they came over to the hotel and we all tried our best to convince each other that there was no way of knowing what had happened after we left. Fire was erratic and crazy. Our homes could be okay. We'd just have to wait and see. By now it was the middle of the night, and a cold front was moving through.

The temperature up in the mountains had dropped 50 degrees and light snow was falling. We dared to dream it had started falling in time.

The next morning, we drove over to the hotel where our friends were staying; it had a big courtyard restaurant, and many evacuees had gathered there to wait for news. I remember sitting with Rex and LaVonne and our mutual friends Mike and Diane, nervously drinking coffee and trading stories and trying not to think too much.

I remember the phone ringing, and hearing our friend Deb, who is married to a volunteer firefighter, fighting back tears and saying, "Honey, I'm so sorry. Your home is gone." Her voice cracked; she hated having to tell us. I kept reassuring her that it was better knowing than to keep wondering.

I remember lots of hugs and not as many tears as you might think; we were all in shock. I remember worrying about what we should do about our looming trip to Florida and how I was going to get out my monthly newsletters. I remember calling our insurance company and scribbling down our claim number. I remember being truly overjoyed when both of our friends' homes turned out to be not only still standing, but undamaged, although the fire had burned to within 50 feet of Rex and LaVonne's back deck before parting like the Red Sea and literally flowing around their home and down the mountain. Later we learned that we'd escaped just in time; our neighbors fleeing from the valley below us watched our home catch on fire. I don't remember much else about that day.

The next time we saw our dream home, it was a smoldering pile of ashes and debris surrounded by a nightmare landscape conjured up by Stephen King. What few trees remained standing were scorched skeletons. The ridge rising up across the valley that had been a variegated carpet of green the day before was a long expanse of twisted, blackened twigs. Our small pond still held water, but the patio stones we'd spent much of the previous summer hauling, fitting and laying had all exploded. Inexplicably, a lone wooden stool stood unscathed beneath the smoldering remains of one of our 200-year old ponderosa pines.

We wandered along the ridge top with our adjustor, trying to avoid smoldering ash-filled stump holes and shaking our heads in disbelief at the total devastation. Fewer than ten trees were still standing and more or less alive, but the sign at the bottom of our driveway that proudly proclaimed we were a certified tree farm somehow survived.

The next few days were a blur of meeting with our adjustor and talking to family and friends. Everyone wanted to know what they could do; our families live far away, and we were staying in a motel, so for the moment the answer was, "Nothing now...just be there for us."

We decided that since we were homeless and our most pressing tasks were notifying everyone on that Call Now/Call Later list and working on our claim, we might as well go to Florida after all and work on it there. A friend of a friend magically convinced United not to charge us to change our flight.

Before we left, our adjustor set us up with a relocation company; they talked to us about where we wanted to live while we sorted through the ashes and decided what to do with the rest of our lives. They sent us to see several homes for rent that delivered most of what was on our wish list: we wanted to be closer to town so we could more easily work on our claim and everything else, but we weren't ready for life in the suburbs. We wanted space, privacy and a break from worrying about wildfires.

We settled on a house with sweeping views of the Devil's Backbone open space, mostly dramatic rock formations and tough mountain vegetation. Not a tree on the property. We signed a six-month lease before we left. State Farm assured us the relocation company would furnish our new digs while we were gone.

We had rented a tiny guest cottage in the residential section of a quiet and mostly forgotten key in Florida. At my makeshift desk by the window I could watch the Gulf and listen to the soothing sounds of the waves rolling in and the birds squawking while I dutifully typed and researched and filled page after page in the handy inventory form LaVonne had created for us. When I couldn't take any more I worked on my monthly newsletters and the new website we were creating for my book on living smartly in bear country.

Neither of us could sleep through the night. At first, whenever I closed my eyes, I would see the fire creeping up our deck posts and into our home. Over and over I'd imagine the things we'd collected over a lifetime melting into the flames. Most days I was up and working again long before the sun came up. Cory spent the days driving into town to buy groceries, running errands and driving from store to store checking prices and making notes, bringing his discoveries back to me like so many treasures washed up on the shore.

The lovely couple we rented our cottage from became good friends; they even invited us to share Easter dinner with the family. I sent out an email update to friends and family almost every morning, and got email hugs in return that helped keep us going. I spent little time on the phone; I now think it was a blessing that reception was terrible.

My reward for working so diligently on the never-ending chronicle of what our life was worth in dollars and cents was a long walk on the beach every morning, and another one before I finally quit for supper. We would walk hand in hand, singing "Stand by Me" and "I Got You Babe." We watched wide-eyed as dolphins swam by, and became experts at spotting fossil shark teeth hiding in the sand. Every night we watched the sun drop into the Gulf in a predictable blaze of orange and pink and gold.

Our mental fog gradually began to clear. The fire may have wiped out our past, but we resolved not to let it take away our future. We contemplated what we really wanted to do with a chapter of our life we'd never expected to write. We thought about moving to Florida. We thought about moving to southern Colorado. We even thought about moving back to the Midwest. But in the end we realized that while our dreams had been scorched, Colorado was home. We didn't want to leave our friends or our lives or be too far from the mountains we loved. By the time we came back from Florida our inventory was 75% complete, and we were ready to start looking for a permanent place to call home.

I know that many people wrestle long and hard with what to do next.

Whether to be brave pioneers and defiantly rebuild their home and trust Mother Nature to someday repair the ruined landscape, or find another place in the hills not yet ravaged and try to dream again, or admit defeat and return to the dreaded suburbs. We didn't want to do any of those things.

We had loved our home and our property and our mountain community with all our heart; it had been a life-long dream come true for us to wake up every day somewhere our hearts called home. But everything green and beautiful that had once surrounded us was now in ashes, and our 365-degree views revealed relentless devastation in all directions. And we didn't think we could live with the stress of rebuilding somewhere else where we would worry and wonder if our number would come up again. We couldn't imagine moving to town and living cheek to jowl with the neighbors. I guess we are just not that sociable despite a lifetime in the people business. Where could we put down new roots and start to grow again?

We had formed an instantaneous bond with the rental agent who found our temporary home. It turned out that her small realty company also handled sales, so we asked her to help us find a new place to call home. We wrote up a long list of wants and needs, and she went to work.

We told her we absolutely did not want another log home; not because we were worried about fire, but because more than a decade of living in one had convinced us that unrelenting maintenance was the price of that particular dream. So we looked at stucco and frame and even brick, but nothing felt right to us. My husband sneered at the hollow doors and plastic moldings and shoddy construction of spacious, beautifully appointed new homes with kitchens and bathrooms to die for, but no character to speak of. I lusted after the gigantic closets that were the size of bedrooms even though I had nothing to put in them. But we just couldn't picture living in any of them.

Reluctantly, we started including log homes in the list. We saw a few we liked, but we didn't love where they were. We had trouble finding a home on some acreage that we could afford that wasn't in the wildfire zone. Buying new property and building from scratch was out of the question for the same reasons.

But the solidness of the logs felt right, so we kept looking. Then one day we walked into a home that had just gone on the market the day before, and fell in love all over again. It was in an older, rural development outside the city limits on a bit over three acres, with a beautiful view of the snow-capped peaks. It had hand-peeled logs, soaring windows and a big covered back porch. The backyard was small by our old standards, but there were quaking aspens and a pond with water lilies and goldfish with no bears and bobcats to eat them and a gurgling stream and waterfall you could hear whenever the windows were open. The neighbors were close enough to walk to, and far enough away for privacy.

We set a closing date for mid-August; my correspondence file from that summer shows dozens of emails to and from our adjustor as we dotted i's and crossed t's. The closer it got to the big day, the faster the email mill churned. There were some anxious days and nights on the phone, but in the end we hit our policy limits and collected all of our checks except for the money that remained from our extended replacement coverage. We planned to use that to make improvements to our 22-year old "new" house. Less than six months after our house burned down we turned the key in the door of our new home.

It would be another month before we moved in for real, not that we had much to move. I would have been happy to sleep on the floor, but we decided we might as well take the time to do all those things that are really hard to do when you have a house full of furniture and stuff. So we replaced the old shake-shingle roof (no longer up to code) with a much safer hail-rated asphalt-shingle one (and saved $400 a year on our homeowners insurance), put in a new furnace and hot-water heater, added air conditioning, refinished the wood floors and carpeted the rest of them, painted all the plaster walls, replaced the kitchen counters, remodeled the master bath and had the old cracked concrete patio covered with stone.

Because we were using our 20% extended replacement coverage, we had to get estimates for everything we wanted to do and have them approved, but our adjustor was great at keeping things moving along. Our friend who'd told us our home had been lost is a cracker-jack general contractor. Despite having just broken her back and gotten married, she managed to find us great subcontractors and made sure we got more than our money's worth.

We stocked our kitchen, splurged on the red leather couch of my dreams, comfy beds and good towels, and decided for the rest of it we'd just try to relax and enjoy the journey and accept the fact that it was going to be a while before our house had that lived-in look.

Today it's starting to seem like home. We do a lot of our shopping at antique malls and thrift stores and estate sales; we don't want it to feel as if we ordered our new life from a catalog. And it turned out to be a good way to stretch our insurance money as well. Now every time we find something we love, we feel as if we're getting another piece of our life back.

We discovered that there were many things we used to have that we didn't want or need anymore. But we also discovered that buying something just like the one we loved and lost often filled a hole in our lives and helped create a link back to memories we were afraid would fade away.

The task of starting over is overwhelming. We've always been the ones on the giving end of a helping hand. To be so badly in need for so very long was a humbling and sobering experience. I really wanted to write about all the ways large and small so many people helped us on our journey back to normal. But I found out that to do it justice would take at least another book. Just to know that so many people were there for us was one of the greatest gifts we've ever received.

Our new neighbors stopped by with baked goods and mums and offers of help. They're all good people. Some of them are becoming good friends. Our family circle closed its arms around us. Everyone set about finding bits and pieces of our pasts...photos, recipes and family treasures. Our empty bookshelves and walls and rooms slowly began to take on new life. Our friends on the mountain helped us every day, in too many ways to count. Friendships that were already strong are now forged forever.

Along the way we learned that we are tougher and stronger than we thought. That when we get knocked down, we eventually get back up again. That it helps to see the glass half-full. That you can be grateful for what you once had even while you mourn its loss. That there is nothing more valuable than friends, family and community. And that if you can laugh at yourself, you can get through anything.

After the fire little remained that even vaguely resembled our home; we took to referring to the pile of ashes and debris as the cremains. On a sunny day in June we went back up to our ridge top with our good friends the Ewings to see if there was anything that could be salvaged, or if it was time to say goodbye and give the demolition company the okay to move ahead.

Masked and gloved and jacketed despite the heat, we doggedly poked about in the rubble. We discovered a delicate porcelain plate that had been my grandmother's; the glaze had melted off, but the plate was fine. We uncovered a set of old cookie cutters that had been inside a tin inside a tin inside a tin, and a small ceramic pitcher that had once held pens and pencils. We found my favorite Santa mug, looking as if Jolly Old Saint Nick had gotten stuck in the chimney. We carefully collected bits and pieces of brightly colored glass melted into fantasy sculptures, remnants of the bottles that had once filled our windows. LaVonne even unearthed several of the agates we'd found on the beach in Oregon. I still don't know how she picked them out of the ashes and dirt, but today they sit in a small glass dish on a table in our entryway.

I love to give special presents, and have always had a habit of shopping year round for gifts. I stored my horde of treasures in a big cupboard in a corner of the basement. LaVonne was over in that corner industriously rooting around when she uncovered a beautiful green pottery vase. Some of the glaze was melted off, but otherwise it was just fine. But here's the strangest thing of all. I'd bought that vase as a gift for her.

Of course, she wouldn't take it. So now it has a place of honor on our new mantel. It survived, just as we did. And it will go on, a bit rough around the edges, just as we will.

Acknowledgments

Having your home burn to the ground in a wildfire does not automatically turn you into a wildfire expert—although the aftermath forces you to become an insurance expert and gives you a lot of insight into woulda-coulda-shoulda.

This book would not have been possible without input, guidance, perspective and technical reviews from people, organizations and agencies with decades of experience in forestry, wildfire preparedness, the science and history of wildfire, wildland firefighting, evacuation and survival, emergency services, dealing with loss and finding the way to recovery, along with the complex world of insurance and catastrophic loss.

I'd like to thank many staff members of the National Fire Protection Association, including the manager of the Firewise Communities Program Michele Steinberg, the director of the Wildand Fire Operations Division Dave Nuss, Associate Project Manager Hylton Haynes, and the manager of the One Stop Data Shop Nancy Schwartz. Thanks also to USDA Forest Service District Forest Ranger Kevin Atchley, Colorado State Forester Mike Hughes, Wildland Fire Manger Dave Zader, Fire Management Specialist Sky Mignery, Silver Star Subdivision Firewise Board Chair Helen McGranahan, Rist Canyon VFD Fire Chief Bob Gann, social scientist Susan I. Stewart, meteorologists Kathy Sabine, Ashton Altieri and Mike Nelson, climatologist Nolan Doesken, Rocky Mountain Insurance Information Institute's Executive Director Carole Walker, writer and researcher Paul Keller, CPA Shannon O'Connor, banker Vivien DeVoe, Mark Wehde team members Janet Schutter and Colleen Miller, and numerous insurance adjustors, insurance agents and experts, many of whom requested to go unnamed, as well as emergency services personnel and city, county, state and federal officials from across the country.

And very special thanks to my publisher LaVonne Ewing, who encouraged me to write this book and whose diligence and patience helped me bring clarity to the incredibly complex.

Thank you to everyone who provided photos, including:

Doug Conarroe, *North Forty News* (pages 61, 68, 77, 78);
LaVonne Ewing (35, 82, 87, 89, 92, 100, 135); Lori Forest (67);
Thia Martin (107); NFPA Firewise Communities Program (20, 21, 29, 36, 37);
Terry Shetler (79); Tony Simons (10, 47); Joe Skelton (81); Darrell Spangler (16)

Wildfire Resources for Homeowners

Preparedness and Safety

Firewise
www.firewise.org
The National Fire Protection Association's (NFPA) **Firewise Communities program** develops local solutions for planning, prevention and wildfire safety. A wealth of resources including downloadable brochures and fact sheets are available, along with interactive modules, demonstration videos and blogs. There are sections for homeowners, communities, firefighters, developers and the media.

Federal Emergency Management Association (FEMA)
www.fema.gov
FEMA's multilayered and complex website is the place to go if you are applying for federal disaster aid or looking for your state's Emergency Management Agency. For wildfire specific information, *www.usfa.fema.gov* has information that's easier to find. To find the Offices of Emergency Management: *www.fema.gov/regional-operations/state-offices-and-agencies-emergency-management*

Ready
www.ready.gov
1-800-BE-Ready
Ready was launched in 2003 to educate and empower people to prepare for and deal with emergencies and disasters. Their website covers a wide range of disasters; search under Wildfire for wildfire mitigation, family disaster planning and preparedness, and recovery guides. Special materials available for children and pets.

U.S. Fire Administration
www.usfa.fema.gov
Wildfire Preparedness is on the home page; many topics from fire prevention to firefighter safety are covered in the Fire Services section. If you search under Publications, then look under Wildfire you will find many free PDF and print publications.

Ready, Set, Go! (RSG)
www.wildlandfires.org
A program launched in 2011 by the International Association of Fire Chiefs to help fire departments teach people who live in high risk wildfire areas and the WUI how to prepare themselves and their property. Find state programs and a wide variety of educational information and materials on the website.

State and Local Resources
To find info on fire conditions and behavior, specific prevention tactics, vegetation, regulations and building codes for your area, visit your state and county governments' websites. If you can't figure out where to go, try searching the topic (i.e. "wildfire prevention") plus your state and/or county name.

American Red Cross
www.redcross.org
Often first on the scene of disasters, the Red Cross plays a major role in setting up and supplying evacuation centers. They also offer preparedness and long-term recovery information and assistance. **Local Red Cross offices** are linked from the home page. Also check *www.redcross.org/prepare/disaster/wildfire* for their *Wildfire Preparedness and Recovery.*

DisasterSafety.org
www.disastersafety.org/wildfire/
As part of its overall mission of reducing property losses, this website was created by the Insurance Institute for Business & Home Safety (IBHS) for homeowners and business owners. It is packed with useful information, including a home assessment checklist, regional guides to protecting your property, risk assessments and much more.

Insurance

Many **insurance carriers** have wildfire preparedness guidelines on their websites as well as home inventory sheets, software and/or mobile apps, but information can be challenging to locate. Look in their Claims Centers or use their search engines.

State Insurance Commissions

Among its many responsibilities, your state's insurance commission is charged with protecting and advocating for consumers. If you have a question that you have not been able to resolve about how a claim is being handled or want to file a complaint, they can investigate and intervene on your behalf.

Insurance Information Institute
www.iii.org

Dedicated to improving the public's understanding of what insurance does and how it works. For information on homeowner's insurance, including average premiums by state, look under the Consumer section. For information on disaster preparedness, look under Disasters. There's also a list of Claims phone numbers for hundreds of insurance companies at: *www.iii.org/articles/ insurance-company-claims-filing-telephone- numbers.html*

Rocky Mountain Insurance Information Association
www.rmiia.org

RMIIA represents property and casualty insurers in Colorado, New Mexico, Utah and Wyoming. Its full-time job is to help consumers, the media and its partners better understand insurance. The website offers in-depth information on a wide variety of topics, and is exceptionally user friendly.

National Association of Public Insurance Adjustors
www.napia.com

United Policyholders
www.uphelp.org

Home Inventory Software/Apps

In addition to inventory forms available from many insurance companies and state and local agencies and governments, check out these two sources:

Insurance Information Institute provides the popular free *Know Your Stuff* software and smart phone apps.
www.iii.org/software

National Association of Insurance Commissioners
provides a free home inventory checklist, tips and free smart phone apps for that let you photograph and capture descriptions of your stuff and store electronically.
www.insureuonline.org/home_inventory_ page.htm

Home Valuation

Software programs and online calculators that help you figure out how much it would cost to rebuild your home:

HMFacts
www.hmfacts.com

AccuCoverage
www.accucoverage.com

Insure to Value
www.bluebook.net/products/insure-to-value

Wildfire Info / Tracking

InciWeb
www.inciweb.org

An excellent source for accurate and up-to-date information about U.S. wildfires. You can track fires by state and fire name; an active fire is generally updated at least daily.

National Interagency Fire Center
www.nifc.gov

This is where to find the monthly and seasonal wildfire outlooks and national fire news. They also provide wildland fire prevention/education teams that can be mobilized to do fire risk assessments and work with communities.

Fire, Fuel, and Smoke Science Program
www.firelab.org

Materials on this website are intended for fire managers and scientists, but interested civilians will find fact sheets, papers, videos and demonstrations that show how fire grows and spreads, how homes ignite, and other aspects of wildland fire behavior.

General Bibliography

Here are just a few of the many references used in preparing this book.
Visit **www.SurvivingWildfire.com** for a full list.

Addressing Community Wildfire Risk: A Review and Assessment of Regulatory and Planning Tools. Clarion Associates. Fire Protection Research Foundation, National Fire Protection Association, 2011.

Brush, Grass and Forest Fires. Marty Ahrens. National Fire Protection Association, Fire Analysis and Research Division, 2010.

Communities at Risk Report. National Association of State Foresters, 2011.

Communities Compatible with Nature. Firewise Communities Program.

Demographic Trends, the Wildland-Urban Interface and Wildfire Management. Roger B. Hammer, Susan I. Stewart, and Voker C. Radeloff. Society and Natural Resources 22:777-782, 2009.

Evaluating Insurance. Daniel Schwarcz. Legal Studies Research Paper Series No. 10-65, 2011.

Family Emergency Plan. FEMA.

Glossary of Wildland Fire Terminology. National Wildfire Coordinating Group, PMS 205, November 2008.

Help After a Disaster: Applicant's Guide to the Individual's and Households Program. FEMA 545. July 2008.

Homeowners Insurance: Don't Forget the Keys. Rocky Mountain Insurance Information Association.

Living with Wildfire: A Guide for Homeowners. The Burn Institute.

Picking Up the Pieces after a Fire. American Red Cross.

Preventing Disasters: Home Ignitability in the Wildland-Urban Interface. Jack D. Cohen. Journal of Forestry 98(3):15-21, 2000.

Ready, Set, Go! Wildfire Preparedness for Farmers, Ranchers and Growers; and *Ready, Set, Go! For Trail Users.* Ventura County, California Fire Department and Ready, Set, Go!

Ready, Set, Go! Your Personal Wildfire Action Plan. Colorado State Fire Chiefs Association, Fire Marshal's Association.

Roadmap to Recovery: How to Navigate the Insurance Claims Process. Rocky Mountain Insurance Information Association.

Safer from the Start, A Guide to Firewise-Friendly Development. Firewise Communities Program.

Saving the Whole Family. American Veterinary Medical Association.

Wildfires and Insurance. Paul Kovacs. Institute for Catastrophic Loss Reduction, ICLR Research Series No. 11, 2001.

Wildfire...Are You Prepared? U.S. Fire Administration, FA-287, August 2004.

Wildfire Fuels and Fuel Reduction. Ross W. Gorte. Congressional Research Service Report for Congress, 7-5700 R40811, 2009.

Wildfire Hazards – A National Threat. U.S. Geological Survey. U.S. Department of the Interior Fact Sheet 2006-3015.

Wildfire Home Assessment & Checklist. Insurance Institute for Business and Home Safety.

Wildfire Safety Guide: Before, During and After a Wildfire. Centers for Disease Control and Prevention.

Index

ABOUT THE AUTHOR

photo by Desariah Santillanez

Award-winning author and researcher Linda Masterson tackles a subject she knows all too well in *Surviving Wildfire: Get Prepared, Stay Alive, Rebuild Your Life (A Handbook for Homeowners)*. In 2011, her home and 72-acre tree farm burned to the ground in a Colorado wildfire, leaving her with little but her laptop, a fierce determination to get back on her feet and get on with her life, and a commitment to helping other homeowners be better prepared.

Masterson has always specialized in turning the complex into the comprehensible. In her job as director of Strategic Planning for Ketchum Communications she provided insight and direction to clients ranging from Procter & Gamble to Campbell Soup. As an award-winning author, her work has appeared in *The New York Times Sunday Magazine, Log Homes Illustrated, Countryside, New Pioneer, Animal Kingdom* and many more. Her handbook, *Living with Bears: A Practical Guide to Bear Country*, has become the book of choice for bear professionals and homeowners alike.

Linda and her husband Cory Phillips now live in a refurbished log home north of Fort Collins and are hard at work replanting their tree farm.

SurvivingWildfire.com

*Also available: **Get Wildfire Smart Pocket Guide**, a companion to the book.*
Quantity discounts and custom imprint program details online.

100% solar & wind powered since 1999
PIXYJACK PRESS INC

PO Box 149   Masonville, CO 80541 USA   **PixyJackPress.com**   *info@pixyjackpress.com*